Workbook for Introduction to Health Care

Miami Dade College Edition

Dakota Mitchell
Lee Haroun

Australia • Brazil • Japan • Korea • Mexico • Singapore • Spain • United Kingdom • United States

CENGAGE
Learning™

**Workbook for Introduction to Health Care
Miami Dade College Edition**

Workbook to Accompany Introduction to Health Care, Third Edition
Mitchell / Haroun

© 2012 Cengage Learning. All rights reserved.

Executive Editors:
Maureen Staudt
Michael Stranz

Senior Project Development Manager:
Linda deStefano

Marketing Specialist:
Courtney Sheldon

Senior Production/Manufacturing Manager:
Donna M. Brown

PreMedia Manager:
Joel Brennecke

Sr. Rights Acquisition Account Manager:
Todd Osborne

Cover Image:
Getty Images*

*Unless otherwise noted, all cover images used by Custom
Solutions, a part of Cengage Learning, have been supplied
courtesy of Getty Images with the exception of the Earthview
cover image, which has been supplied by the National
Aeronautics and Space Administration (NASA).

ALL RIGHTS RESERVED. No part of this work covered by the copyright herein
may be reproduced, transmitted, stored or used in any form or by any means
graphic, electronic, or mechanical, including but not limited to photocopying,
recording, scanning, digitizing, taping, Web distribution, information networks,
or information storage and retrieval systems, except as permitted under
Section 107 or 108 of the 1976 United States Copyright Act, without the prior
written permission of the publisher.

For product information and technology assistance, contact us at
Cengage Learning Customer & Sales Support, 1-800-354-9706

For permission to use material from this text or product,
submit all requests online at **cengage.com/permissions**
Further permissions questions can be emailed to
permissionrequest@cengage.com

This book contains select works from existing Cengage Learning resources and
was produced by Cengage Learning Custom Solutions for collegiate use. As such,
those adopting and/or contributing to this work are responsible for editorial
content accuracy, continuity and completeness.

Compilation © 2011 Cengage Learning
ISBN-13: 978-1-133-68989-8

ISBN-10: 1-133-68989-2

Cengage Learning
5191 Natorp Boulevard
Mason, Ohio 45040
USA
Cengage Learning is a leading provider of customized learning solutions with
office locations around the globe, including Singapore, the United Kingdom,
Australia, Mexico, Brazil, and Japan. Locate your local office at:
international.cengage.com/region.

Cengage Learning products are represented in Canada by Nelson Education, Ltd.
For your lifelong learning solutions, visit **www.cengage.com/custom.**
Visit our corporate website at **www.cengage.com.**

Printed in the United States of America

Table of Contents

© 2012 Cengage Learning. All Rights Reserved. May not be scanned, copied or duplicated, or posted to a publicly accessible website, in whole or in part.

© 2012 Cengage Learning. All Rights Reserved. May not be scanned, copied or duplicated, or posted to a publicly accessible website, in whole or in part.

To the Learner

Introduction to Health Care, third edition, is designed as an introductory text for learners who are entering college-level health care programs or for those who believe they may be interested in pursuing a career in health care. The fundamentals common to all health care occupations are presented in this full-color text to create a foundation on which learners can build when they take their specific occupational courses. The topics included are appropriate for occupations that involve direct patient care, such as nursing and dental assisting, as well as those that provide support services, such as health information technology and pharmacy technician. The goal of the text is to present a broad base of health care essentials. Therefore, skills and procedures that apply only to specific occupations are not included.

ORGANIZATION OF THE WORKBOOK

The purpose of this workbook is to provide you with additional practice to help you master content in the textbook. Each chapter in the workbook corresponds to the same chapter in the textbook and begins with the statement of chapter objectives. A variety of questions and exercises are included to help reinforce in different ways the material you have learned. Types of questions and exercises included in the workbook include defining terms, matching, identification, true/false, true/false rewrite, multiple choice, completion, ordering, and labeling. Additionally, each chapter includes two critical thinking scenarios to encourage you to think about and apply concepts learned in the chapter. Procedure checklists are also included to help you assess your mastery of the basic hands-on skills included in the text.

As you proceed through each chapter of the text, complete the activities provided in this workbook to reinforce the material presented in class.

The following steps are recommended for using the textbook and workbook:

1. Read the chapter objectives.

2. Study the material presented in the text.

3. Listen carefully to the instructor.

4. Take comprehensive notes.

5. Ask questions.

6. Complete the questions and exercises in the workbook.

7. Review any concepts missed while completing the workbook exercises.

This workbook was prepared as a tool to help you learn. The authors hope this tool will help you master the introductory health care concepts necessary for success in your chosen career.

© 2012 Cengage Learning. All Rights Reserved. May not be scanned, copied or duplicated, or posted to a publicly accessible website, in whole or in part.

UNIT 1
Health Care Today

© 2012 Cengage Learning. All Rights Reserved. May not be scanned, copied or duplicated, or posted to a publicly accessible website, in whole or in part.

CHAPTER 1

Your Career in Health Care

LEARNING OBJECTIVES

Studying and applying the material in this chapter will help you to:

- Describe the essential core qualities demonstrated by effective health care professionals.
- Describe the major kinds of approvals whose purpose is to ensure the competency of health care professionals.
- List the personal factors that should be considered when choosing a health care career.
- Describe the four categories of health care careers and give examples of three occupational titles for each category.
- State the educational and certification, registration, and/or licensing requirements of occupations in which you are interested.
- Explain the meaning of "thinking like a health care professional."
- Apply the five-step problem-solving process to make effective decisions.
- Practice the habits that contribute to both academic and professional success.
- Use study techniques that complement your preferred learning style.
- Explain the meaning of "learning for mastery."
- Describe the advantages and challenges of adult learners.
- List five organizational and time-management techniques recommended for adult learners.

© 2012 Cengage Learning. All Rights Reserved. May not be scanned, copied or duplicated, or posted to a publicly accessible website, in whole or in part.

VOCABULARY REVIEW

Definitions

Write the definition of each of the following words or terms.

1. bias

_____

_____

_____

2. integrity

_____

_____

_____

3. learning style

_____

_____

_____

4. manual dexterity

_____

_____

_____

5. reliable

_____

_____

_____

Matching 1

Match the following terms with their correct definitions.

_____ 1. career ladder

_____ 2. certification

_____ 3. licensure

_____ 4. registration

_____ 5. scope of practice

A. process of determining whether an individual has met predetermined standards

B. granting of permission to legally perform certain acts

C. skills that practitioners of a specific occupation may legally perform

D. levels within an occupational area that require different amounts of education and training

E. placement on an official list after meeting educational and testing requirements

© 2012 Cengage Learning. All Rights Reserved. May not be scanned, copied or duplicated, or posted to a publicly accessible website, in whole or in part.

Matching 2

Match the following terms with their correct definitions.

——— 1. assessment

A. belief not necessarily based on facts

——— 2. objective

B. describes information that cannot be observed or measured

——— 3. opinion

C. factual approach to a situation

——— 4. problem-solving process

D. factors, such as a fever, that are observable or measurable

——— 5. signs

E. indication of disease or injury experienced by a patient

——— 6. subjective

F. gathering of information to help determine a patient's condition

——— 7. symptom

G. sequence of steps used to help find solutions

Word Fill

Complete the following sentences by filling in the missing words.

diagnostic   therapeutic   kinesthetic   visual
auditory

1. Nursing is an example of a/an _____ occupation.

2. Radiologic technology is an example of a/an _____ occupation.

3. A good method for a/an _____ learner to acquire new anatomical terms is by studying illustrations of the body systems.

4. Reading a list of medical terms aloud is a good way for a/an _____ learner to master new vocabulary.

5. A/an _____ learner would likely benefit by assembling a kit of the skeleton to learn the names of the bones.

CHAPTER REVIEW

Identification

Place an "X" in front of each therapeutic occupation.

——— 1. dental hygienist

——— 2. diagnostic medical sonographer

——— 3. pharmacy technician

© 2012 Cengage Learning. All Rights Reserved. May not be scanned, copied or duplicated, or posted to a publicly accessible website, in whole or in part.

_____ 4. home health aide

_____ 5. dietetic technician

_____ 6. mental health technician

_____ 7. medical transcriptionist

_____ 8. laboratory technician

_____ 9. medical assistant

_____ 10. paramedic

True/False

Indicate whether the following statements are true (T) or false (F).

_____ 1. Some health care occupations have more than one form of approval or certification.

_____ 2. Many adult learners are at a disadvantage when they try to compete with younger learners.

_____ 3. Some certifying and licensing boards require that test applicants graduate from an accredited program.

_____ 4. Manual dexterity refers to an individual's ability to observe.

_____ 5. The majority of learning involves memorizing facts, such as medical terms and the steps for performing procedures.

_____ 6. Individuals who have been convicted of specific crimes cannot take the certification exams for certain health care occupations.

_____ 7. Natural abilities are an important consideration when choosing a health care career.

_____ 8. Learning for mastery means studying the information required to pass tests.

_____ 9. Good instructors spend most class time telling learners what they need to know to be successful in their occupations.

_____ 10. Understanding why something is done in health care is as important as knowing how to do it.

Multiple Choice

Circle the best answer for each of the following questions. There is only one correct answer to each question.

1. The first step in the 5-step problem-solving process is to _____.

    A. gather information needed to solve the problem
    B. identify the real problem
    C. decide if the problem is worth trying to solve

© 2012 Cengage Learning. All Rights Reserved. May not be scanned, copied or duplicated, or posted to a publicly accessible website, in whole or in part.

2. What is the last step when using the 5-step problem-solving process?

    A. take action by implementing a solution
    B. review the results of the alternative chosen
    C. choose an alternative

3. Which of the following individuals best demonstrates the meaning of "thinking like a health care professional"?

    A. Dan, a surgical technologist, has learned a series of steps that he always uses when preparing a patient for surgery.
    B. Angie, a laboratory technician, always collects the materials she will need before performing lab tests.
    C. Jacob, a veterinary technician, brings to the veterinarian's attention unusual behavior in a dog that was brought in for a test.

4. Which of the following challenges is most likely to be faced by an adult returning to school?

    A. finding time to study
    B. competing with younger students
    C. lack of self-confidence

5. Which of the following activities would most likely work best for a visual learner who is studying the characteristics of good medical documentation?

    A. read about each of the characteristics
    B. practice creating samples of medical documentation
    C. say the characteristics out loud

6. Brandon is interested in the field of physical therapy, but does not currently have a lot of time or the financial resources to attend school. Which of the following physical therapy careers would be best under these circumstances?

    A. physical therapist
    B. physical therapist aide
    C. physical therapist assistant

7. Which of the following careers would best suit an individual who enjoys working with detailed paperwork?

    A. optometric assistant
    B. magnetic resonance technologist
    C. coding specialist

8. Which of the following certifications is never voluntary?

    A. licensure
    B. certification
    C. approval

© 2012 Cengage Learning. All Rights Reserved. May not be scanned, copied or duplicated, or posted to a publicly accessible website, in whole or in part.

9. Jeff enjoys the lecture portion of his *Introduction To Health Care* class, but dislikes any kind of group work with his classmates. How is this likely to affect his future career success?

    A. no effect as long as he performs his work
    B. positively because he will not waste his time socializing with coworkers
    C. negatively because work in health care is performed by teams

10. Which of the following individuals is expressing an opinion?

    A. Mike's belief that people who don't have jobs and lack medical insurance are too lazy to work
    B. James statement that, according the Bureau of Labor Statistics, the unemployment rate in the United States is 9.5 percent
    C. Dan's desire to help the unemployed by volunteering at a local community center

Matching 3

Match the following core qualities of health care professionals with the example that best demonstrates that quality.

_____ 1. care about others	A.	use courtesy with coworkers
_____ 2. have integrity	B.	never take supplies for your own use
_____ 3. be dependable	C.	accept responsibility for an error made at work
_____ 4. work well with others	D.	read articles that relate to your career area
_____ 5. be flexible	E.	return from lunch break on schedule
_____ 6. be willing to learn	F.	show respect to a difficult patient
_____ 7. strive to be cost conscious	G.	exchange work days to help at a weekend flu clinic

Completion

Use the words in the list to complete the following statements.

technologist	license	assistant	registration
associate's	certification	bachelor's	standards
scope of practice	aide		

1. _____ for health care professionals are set by various agencies and organizations to ensure the professionals are competent. .

2. _____ means being placed on an official list after meeting certain educational and testing requirements.

3. The general term for describing the process of determining the competence of a health care professional is _____.

4. An individual who is legally approved to work in a specific occupation receives a/an _____.

© 2012 Cengage Learning. All Rights Reserved. May not be scanned, copied or duplicated, or posted to a publicly accessible website, in whole or in part.

5. The list of duties that can be performed by practitioners of a specific occupation is called its _____.

6. The health care professional who has less education than an occupational therapy assistant is an occupational therapy _____.

7. A physical therapist has more education than a physical therapist _____.

8. A/An _____ degree is usually completed in two years

9. A/An _____ degree is usually completed in four years.

10. In most occupational areas, a/an _____ has more education than a technician.

Ordering

Place the following positions on the emergency medical career ladder in the order of education required. Put a numeral 1 before the position requiring the most education, a 2 before the next, and so on.

_____ 1. first responder

_____ 2. EMT – Intermediate/99

_____ 3. paramedic

_____ 4. EMT – Basic

_____ 5. EMT – Intermediate/85

Critical Thinking Scenarios

Read each scenario. Think about the information presented in the text, and then answer each question.

1. Craig finds it difficult to master new material unless he actually does something with it. For example, when learning a new procedure, it is hard for him to simply visualize the steps to follow.

   A. What type of learner is Craig?

   _____

   _____

   _____

   B. What study techniques can he use to best learn new information, such as the steps in the problem-solving process?

   _____

   _____

   _____

© 2012 Cengage Learning. All Rights Reserved. May not be scanned, copied or duplicated, or posted to a publicly accessible website, in whole or in part.

2. Mr. Taylor, a patient recovering from knee replacement surgery, tells Carla, a physical therapist assistant, that he is experiencing pain as he performs the exercises prescribed for him.

    A. Is the pain he is experiencing a sign or a symptom?

    _____

    _____

    _____

    B. What is the difference between a sign and a symptom?

    _____

    _____

    _____

    C. Is his pain an example of objective or subjective data?

    _____

    _____

    _____

© 2012 Cengage Learning. All Rights Reserved. May not be scanned, copied or duplicated, or posted to a publicly accessible website, in whole or in part.

CHAPTER 2

Current Health Care Systems and Trends

LEARNING OBJECTIVES

Studying and applying the material in this chapter will help you to:

- Describe 10 significant events in the history of health care that changed the way care was delivered.

- Describe the major forces in the health care industry today.

- Describe the levels of care offered by the modern hospital.

- List 10 ambulatory health care facilities and give examples of the type of services offered by each one.

- Describe the major types of long-term care facilities.

- Provide examples of health care services and care that can be provided in the patient's home.

- Explain the purpose of hospice.

- List typical services offered by federal, state, and local health agencies.

- Explain the concept of "wellness."

- Describe the types of complementary and alternative medicine being practiced in the United States today.

- List five challenges facing health care today and explain how the health care professional can contribute to their resolution.

© 2012 Cengage Learning. All Rights Reserved. May not be scanned, copied or duplicated, or posted to a publicly accessible website, in whole or in part.

VOCABULARY REVIEW

Definitions

Write the definition of each of the following words or terms.

1. gene therapy

   _____

   _____

   _____

2. Medicaid

   _____

   _____

   _____

3. palliative

   _____

   _____

   _____

4. pandemic

   _____

   _____

   _____

5. psychosomatic

   _____

   _____

   _____

6. targeted drug therapy

   _____

   _____

   _____

7. vital statistics

   _____

   _____

   _____

8. wellness

   _____

   _____

   _____

© 2012 Cengage Learning. All Rights Reserved. May not be scanned, copied or duplicated, or posted to a publicly accessible website, in whole or in part.

Matching 1

Match the following terms with their correct definitions.

_____ 1. acupuncture

_____ 2. alternative medicine

_____ 3. chiropractic

_____ 4. complementary medicine

_____ 5. expanding consciousness

_____ 6. holistic medicine

_____ 7. homeopathy

_____ 8. integrative medicine

_____ 9. massage therapy

_____ 10. osteopathy

A. nontraditional treatment used along with conventional medicine

B. combination of treatments from conventional medicine with complementary and/or alternative medicine

C. treatment involving insertion of tiny needles into the body

D. treatment involving manipulating the spine to relieve pressure on nerves

E. health care approach that considers all the following components: physical, mental, emotional, and spiritual

F. medical theory that the body protects itself when the musculoskeletal system is in good order

G. treatment of disorders with substances that cause symptoms of the disorders

H. approach to health care that focuses on patients' possibilities rather than their limitations

I. treatment in which muscles are rubbed and kneaded

J. nontraditional treatment used instead of conventional medicine

© 2012 Cengage Learning. All Rights Reserved. May not be scanned, copied or duplicated, or posted to a publicly accessible website, in whole or in part.

Word Fill

Complete the following sentences by filling in the missing words.

intermediate nursing care facility	continuing care community	psychiatric	adult foster home
inpatient	assisted living residence	skilled nursing facility	outpatient
hospice	nursing home		

1. A/an _____ provides personal care, meals, and supervision in a home-like setting for up to five or six residents.

2. A large live-in facility that provides housing, meals, and personal care is called a/an _____.

3. A/an _____ provides services at one location that range from independent living to nursing home care.

4. _____ is a service or facility that provides care and support for individuals who are dying.

5. _____ refers to being admitted to and treated in a hospital.

6. A nursing home that provides personal care, but not on a 24-hour basis, is called a/an _____.

7. A/an _____ is the general term for a live-in facility that provides nursing and personal care.

8. Medical services provided to patients who are not admitted to a hospital are called _____ services.

9. In a/an _____ hospital, patients are treated for mental and behavioral disorders.

10. A nursing home that provides 24-hour nursing care, along with personal care, is called a/an _____.

CHAPTER REVIEW

True/False

Indicate whether the following statements are true (T) or false (F).

_____ 1. The typical lifespan in ancient times was only 45 years.

_____ 2. The Greek physician Hippocrates of Cos has been called the Father of Medicine.

_____ 3. The plagues of the Middle Ages killed more than half the population of Europe.

_____ 4. In the 17th century, William Harvey proposed the first theory of contagious diseases.

© 2012 Cengage Learning. All Rights Reserved. May not be scanned, copied or duplicated, or posted to a publicly accessible website, in whole or in part.

_____ 5. The microscope was invented in the mid 1800s.

_____ 6. The discovery that quinine treated malaria confirmed the theory that specific diseases have specific cures.

_____ 7. For many centuries, it was believed that mucous from a head cold was produced by the brain.

_____ 8. At one time, when diseases were not well understood, 2400 different diseases were "identified" because of slight differences in symptoms.

_____ 9. Before the mid-1700s, mental illness was not recognized as a disease, but thought to be the result of being possessed by the devil.

_____ 10. Edward Jenner demonstrated that vaccinations could be an effective preventive technique for smallpox.

_____ 11. Anesthesia was introduced by surgeons in the early 1900s.

_____ 12. Louis Pasteur developed the germ theory by proving that specific bacteria caused specific diseases.

_____ 13. The theory of psychoanalysis to treat mental illness was developed by Sigmund Freud.

_____ 14. Large-scale vaccination programs were started in the mid-1800s.

_____ 15. The influenza pandemic of 1918 killed about 2,000,000 people.

_____ 16. Vitamins and their effect on the human body were discovered in the 20th century.

_____ 17. In the 20th century, the scientific approach became the principal basis for the practice of medicine.

_____ 18. AIDS was identified as a disease in the 1960s.

_____ 19. Widespread media, such as the Internet, have decreased the spread of fraudulent quick-curing health products.

_____ 20. The first "test tube" baby was born in 1978.

True/False Rewrite

Please rewrite the bold part of the sentence to make the statement true.

1. Home care is **limited to basic services** such as nursing and assistance with personal care.

   _____

   _____

   _____

© 2012 Cengage Learning. All Rights Reserved. May not be scanned, copied or duplicated, or posted to a publicly accessible website, in whole or in part.

2. Medicare covers **all the costs** of home health services.

_____

_____

_____

3. Home health agencies are generally **not regulated.**

_____

_____

_____

4. Most insurance companies cover the cost of **anyone** hired to provide health care in the patient's home.

_____

_____

_____

5. Occupational therapists help patients **regain movement and increase their physical stamina**.

_____

_____

_____

6. The National Institutes of Health **provide treatment** for chronic diseases such as cancer.

_____

_____

_____

7. **Local health departments** license health care personnel and facilities.

_____

_____

_____

8. Sanitation and insect control measures are generally conducted **by private companies**.

_____

_____

_____

9. The U.S. Occupational Safety and Health Administration **ensures that drugs are pure, safe, and effective**.

_____

_____

_____

© 2012 Cengage Learning. All Rights Reserved. May not be scanned, copied or duplicated, or posted to a publicly accessible website, in whole or in part.

10. The Centers for Disease Control and Prevention is **supported by private financial donations**.

_____

_____

_____

Matching 2

Match the following facilities with the service offered in each.

—— 1. adult day care facility   A. treatment and care for cancer or other specific condition

—— 2. dental office   B. treatment for conditions that need immediate attention

—— 3. diagnostic center   C. classes on nutrition and exercise

—— 4. urgent care center   D. diagnosis and treatment of various health conditions

—— 5. laboratory   E. activities, meals, and supervision for older and disabled individuals

—— 6. medical office   F. tests such as X-ray and ultrasound

—— 7. rehabilitation center   G. physical and occupational therapy

—— 8. specialty clinic   H. operations, such as tonsil removal

—— 9. surgical center   I. tests on blood and other body fluids

——10. wellness center   J. care of the teeth

Short Answer

Read each question. Think about the information presented in the text, and then answer each question.

1. What is the purpose of hospice?

_____

_____

_____

2. What is the currently held meaning of wellness?

_____

_____

_____

© 2012 Cengage Learning. All Rights Reserved. May not be scanned, copied or duplicated, or posted to a publicly accessible website, in whole or in part.

3. What are five challenges facing the health care community today?

_____

_____

_____

4. What is the meaning of "expanding consciousness"?

_____

_____

_____

5. List at least five reasons for the increasing cost of health care.

_____

_____

_____

6. Which part of the population is the heaviest user of health care services?

_____

_____

_____

7. What are three results of the specialization of medicine and health care?

_____

_____

_____

8. How much do economists expect Americans to spend on health care in the year 2018?

_____

_____

_____

9. What is currently the most widely used medical treatment?

_____

_____

_____

10. What are three reasons for the relatively high rate of infant mortality in the United States?

_____

_____

_____

© 2012 Cengage Learning. All Rights Reserved. May not be scanned, copied or duplicated, or posted to a publicly accessible website, in whole or in part.

Completion

Use the words in the list to complete the following statements:

traditional Chinese medicine	reiki	meditation	acupuncture
aromatherapy	homeopathy	ayurveda	naturopathy
chiropractic	reflexology		

1. _____ is an ancient Chinese medicine treatment that uses needles to reduce pain.

2. The use of the hands to manipulate the spine to relieve pressure on the nerves is called _____.

3. The medical system in which symptom-producing substances are administered based on the theory that "like cures like" is _____.

4. _____ is the theory of medicine that draws on nature and emphasizes treating the causes rather than just the symptoms of diseases and disorders.

5. _____ is based on balancing and maintaining the body's energy flow.

6. Treatment that involves inhaling the scents of plant oils is called _____.

7. The practice of _____ by individuals has been found to help them integrate their physical and mental aspects.

8. _____ is a 5000-year-old system of medicine practiced in India.

9. _____ is based on the theory that parts of the bottom of the feet correspond to specific parts of the body.

10. Practitioners of _____ use their hands to transmit healing energy to the body.

Ordering

Place the following levels of care offered in a hospital in order from the highest to the lowest.

_____ 1. general unit

_____ 2. trauma center

_____ 3. intensive care unit

_____ 4. transitional care unit

_____ 5. emergency room

© 2012 Cengage Learning. All Rights Reserved. May not be scanned, copied or duplicated, or posted to a publicly accessible website, in whole or in part.

Critical Thinking Scenarios

Read each scenario. Think about the information presented in the text, and then answer each question.

1. James's employer does not provide health insurance as a benefit. James has a chronic back problem and is finding it difficult to find affordable insurance.

    A. What is the term for conditions such as James's back problem?

    _____

    _____

    _____

    B. What are two other groups of individuals who find it very difficult to purchase health insurance?

    _____

    _____

    _____

    C. What is occurring that may help people such as James to find health care insurance?

    _____

    _____

    _____

2. Erin is beginning her career as an occupational therapy assistant in a rehabilitation hospital. She would like to set a good example for her patients.

    A. What are five behaviors that contribute to good health?

    _____

    _____

    _____

    B. What are the three leading causes of death in the United States that can in some cases be prevented by good health habits?

    _____

    _____

    _____

© 2012 Cengage Learning. All Rights Reserved. May not be scanned, copied or duplicated, or posted to a publicly accessible website, in whole or in part.

CHAPTER 3

Ethical and Legal Responsibilities

LEARNING OBJECTIVES

Studying and applying the material in this chapter will help you to:

- Explain the meaning of ethics and its importance in the practice of health care.
- State the purpose of professional codes of ethics.
- Explain the meaning of values and how they influence personal and professional behavior.
- Describe the relationship between ethics and law.
- List the eight major ethical principles that apply to health care and give examples of the laws that support each.
- Explain how each of the following presents ethical challenges to the health care community: euthanasia, organ transplants, stem-cell research, and rationing of care.
- Explain the importance of patient consent and the possible consequences when actions are taken without the patient's consent.
- Give the definitions of express and implied consent.
- Describe the two major forms of advance directives.
- List the signs of child and elder abuse and state the actions that health care professionals should take in cases of suspected abuse.
- Explain the purpose of the federal schedule of controlled substances.
- Describe the importance of patient confidentiality and possible legal consequences when it is breached.
- Give examples of how the health care professional applies ethics on the job.

© 2012 Cengage Learning. All Rights Reserved. May not be scanned, copied or duplicated, or posted to a publicly accessible website, in whole or in part.

VOCABULARY REVIEW

Definitions

Write the definition of each of the following legal words or terms.

1. adult (legal)

   _____

   _____

   _____

2. agent

   _____

   _____

   _____

3. damages

   _____

   _____

   _____

4. emancipated minor

   _____

   _____

   _____

5. euthanasia

   _____

   _____

   _____

6. invasive procedure

   _____

   _____

   _____

7. mercy killing

   _____

   _____

   _____

8. respondeat superior

   _____

   _____

   _____

© 2012 Cengage Learning. All Rights Reserved. May not be scanned, copied or duplicated, or posted to a publicly accessible website, in whole or in part.

9. stem cell

_____

_____

_____

Matching 1

Match the following terms with their correct definitions.

_____ 1. advance directive

_____ 2. consent

_____ 3. contract

_____ 4. designation of health care surrogate

_____ 5. express consent

_____ 6. express contract

_____ 7. implied consent

_____ 8. implied contract

_____ 9. informed consent

_____ 10. living will

A. agreement reached after the parties have discussed specific terms and conditions

B. legal document in which individuals appoint specific person(s) to act on their behalf if they become unable to make health care decisions for themselves

C. actions of the parties form an unwritten agreement

D. general term for permission given

E. written documents that explain a patient's wishes regarding health care

F. part of an advance directive that outlines the type and extent of medical care to be given

G. formal promise that is enforceable by law

H. permission given by actions, such as making an appointment with a doctor

I. permission for a procedure to be performed after it and any possible consequences have been explained

J. permission given in writing

© 2012 Cengage Learning. All Rights Reserved. May not be scanned, copied or duplicated, or posted to a publicly accessible website, in whole or in part.

Matching 2

Match the following terms with their correct definitions.

_____ 1. autonomy

_____ 2. code of ethics

_____ 3. confidentiality

_____ 4. discreet

_____ 5. ethical dilemma

_____ 6. ethics

_____ 7. justice

_____ 8. legislation

_____ 9. principles

_____ 10. protocols

_____ 11. values

A. intended to be kept secret; right to privacy

B. system of principles used to determine right and wrong

C. laws

D. beliefs about what is important that provide a foundation for making decisions

E. fundamental truths

F. taking care with what is said and respecting privacy

G. self-determination

H. standard methods for performing tasks and procedures

I. fairness

J. situation in which contradicting ethical principles collide

K. collection of principles to guide right conduct

Word Fill

Complete the following sentences by filling in the missing words.

negligence	libel	defamation of character	slander
breach of contract	assault	false imprisonment	battery
malpractice	fraud		

1. A nurse threatening a child with a spanking is an example of _____.

2. If a patient states he does not want a treatment and the physician performs it anyway, the physician may be charged with _____.

3. A patient who refuses to pay his dental bill for a crown he agreed to have made is committing a/an _____.

4. _____ is a legal charge for disclosing unauthorized information that could harm the reputation of another person.

5. A mentally competent patient who is hospitalized against his wishes may charge the hospital with _____.

© 2012 Cengage Learning. All Rights Reserved. May not be scanned, copied or duplicated, or posted to a publicly accessible website, in whole or in part.

6. Making claims that an unproven method of treatment will cure cancer is an example of _____.

7. Making a written statement that might harm a person's reputation may result in a charge of _____.

8. A post-surgical patient who suffers an injury when his physical therapist recommends an obviously inappropriate exercise may decide to sue the therapist for _____.

9. _____ means the failure to provide the standard of care expected of a professional with certain training and experience.

10. Making false, harmful statements about someone whose reputation is then hurt might result in a charge of _____.

CHAPTER REVIEW

True/False

Indicate whether the following statements are true (T) or false (F).

_____ 1. It is correct to inform a patient if you believe her physician has not approved the most effective medication for her.

_____ 2. Health care professionals should not become involved in health care politics.

_____ 3. Controlled substances cannot be legally prescribed by physicians or other health care providers.

_____ 4. Returning late from lunch and breaks is a form of dishonesty.

_____ 5. It is acceptable practice to have patient sign-in registers open on the reception desk of a medical office.

_____ 6. Health care professionals must take care when being optimistic with patients about their treatment outcomes.

_____ 7. Advances in technology have made it difficult to define the meaning of "life."

_____ 8. Withdrawing certain types of artificial life support has become widely acceptable.

_____ 9. Euthanasia means giving comfort measures, such as medication and loving care, as a patient is dying.

_____ 10. Only two states have legalized what is known as mercy killing.

_____ 11. Most dying patients find their approaching death to be depressing and prefer not to talk about it.

_____ 12. Organs can only be taken from individuals who gave permission before their death for their removal.

_____ 13. When many patients are waiting for a limited supply of suitable organs, younger patients are generally given priority for receiving a transplant.

© 2012 Cengage Learning. All Rights Reserved. May not be scanned, copied or duplicated, or posted to a publicly accessible website, in whole or in part.

_____ 14. If a child appears to have been physically abused, patient confidentiality prevents health care professionals from reporting suspected abuse.

_____ 15. Patients who are mentally competent have the right to refuse medical treatment.

Multiple Choice

Circle the best answer for each of the following questions. There is only one correct answer to each question.

1. Amy is careful never to reveal information about her patients to anyone who is not entitled to know about their condition. Amy is being _____.

    A. autonomous
    B. discreet
    C. just

2. Violating a patient's right to privacy might result in a _____.

    A. breach of contract
    B. charge of fraud
    C. lawsuit

3. In which of the following situations would giving out information not authorized by a patient be legal?

    A. the patient's injuries were caused by violence, such as a shooting
    B. the patient's sister wants to know details about his condition before travelling to see him
    C. the patient is being cared for at a hospital supported by public funds

4. The guidelines created by the Health Insurance Portability and Accountability Act (HIPAA) are designed to _____.

    A. protect the privacy of patient medical records
    B. control rising health care expenses
    C. provide funding for expanded health insurance for the poor

5. While mowing the lawn, Al experiences chest pains and goes to the emergency room of the hospital nearest his home, where he is seen immediately. His actions and those of the treating physician are an example of a/an _____.

    A. breach of contract
    B. express contract
    C. implied contract

6. Which of the following is NOT a component of a legal contract?

    A. acceptance
    B. offer
    C. consent

7. A medical assistant may be the legal agent of the physician for whom he works. This means that the medical assistant _____.

    A. has the authority to represent the physician
    B. is required to follow the instructions of the physician
    C. is paid by the physician

© 2012 Cengage Learning. All Rights Reserved. May not be scanned, copied or duplicated, or posted to a publicly accessible website, in whole or in part.

8. If a pharmacist makes an error when filling a prescription because he isn't paying full attention to his work, this is an example of _____.

   A. damages
   B. negligence
   C. respondeat superior

9. A key factor in preventing malpractice lawsuits is to _____.

   A. develop good interpersonal relationships with patients
   B. ensure that all treatments have successful results
   C. enter into written contracts with patients

10. Alisa observes a coworker engaging in illegal behavior on the job. She should _____.

    A. mind her own business
    B. confront the coworker about her behavior
    C. report what she observes to her supervisor

Short Answer

Read each question. Think about the information presented in the text, and then answer each question.

1. Stem cells hold promise to cure many diseases and conditions caused by injuries. Why have some people been opposed to stem cell research?

   _____
   _____
   _____

2. What are five signs that a child may have been physically abused?

   _____
   _____
   _____

3. What are five criteria developed by the American Medical Association to make decisions about who should receive organ transplants?

   _____
   _____
   _____

4. What are five factors that must be explained to patients when seeking their informed consent for a surgical procedure?

   _____
   _____
   _____

© 2012 Cengage Learning. All Rights Reserved. May not be scanned, copied or duplicated, or posted to a publicly accessible website, in whole or in part.

5. What information is contained in a living will?

    _____

    _____

    _____

6. Some restrictions that insurance providers use to control costs present ethical dilemmas for health care professionals. List five such restrictions.

    _____

    _____

    _____

7. What unintended result did Massachusetts encounter when it required every resident to obtain health insurance?

    _____

    _____

    _____

8. List five types of elder abuse, a growing problem in the United States.

    _____

    _____

    _____

9. What is the purpose of the Occupational Safety and Health Act of 1970?

    _____

    _____

    _____

10. Give four examples of commonly encountered health care fraud.

    _____

    _____

    _____

Completion

Use the words in the list to complete the following statements:

laws	Hippocrates	interests	responsible
code of ethics	ethical dilemma	consequences	values
ethical principles	technology		

© 2012 Cengage Learning. All Rights Reserved. May not be scanned, copied or duplicated, or posted to a publicly accessible website, in whole or in part.

1. The life of a young pregnant woman is in danger due to her pregnancy. Deciding whether to save the mother or the unborn child is an example of a/an _____.

2. The _____ of a society are influenced by its history and the religions practiced by its members.

3. The oath developed over 2000 years ago to guide the conduct of physicians was developed by _____.

4. Advances in medical _____ have presented today's health care community with many new ethical problems.

5. Most organizations for health care professionals have developed a/an _____ to guide the conduct of their members.

6. The belief an individual holds about the importance of friendship is influenced by his _____.

7. Societies create _____ based on their ethical principles in order to enforce the behavior that supports these principles.

8. The American legal system is based on the belief that individuals should be _____ for their own actions.

9. Well-intentioned laws sometimes have unintended _____ that create rather than solve problems.

10. There is sometimes a conflict between the _____ of patients and the laws and rules that health care professionals must follow.

Critical Thinking

Read each scenario. Think about the information presented in the text, and then answer each question.

1. Carolyn is a physical therapy assistant who has been visiting the home of Mr. Sterns, an 82-year-old man, twice a week. She has noticed that his appearance has deteriorated recently and that he seems unclean with a poor, unwashed odor. He also seems nervous with Carolyn when his son Harold is present.

   A. What might be the problem with Mr. Sterns?

   _____

   _____

   _____

   B. If his situation gets worse and he tells Carolyn he is afraid of his son, what should she do?

   _____

   _____

   _____

© 2012 Cengage Learning. All Rights Reserved. May not be scanned, copied or duplicated, or posted to a publicly accessible website, in whole or in part.

2. Craig Samuels has become a frequent repeat visitor to the clinic in which Erin is a medical assistant. Craig complains of various pains and always asks for a prescription for pain medication.

    A. What might be Craig's real reason for visiting the clinic?

    _____

    _____

    _____

    B. What should Erin do?

    _____

    _____

    _____

    C. How does the government control medications such as those that are prescribed for pain?

    _____

    _____

    _____

© 2012 Cengage Learning. All Rights Reserved. May not be scanned, copied or duplicated, or posted to a publicly accessible website, in whole or in part.

UNIT 2
The Language of Health Care

© 2012 Cengage Learning. All Rights Reserved. May not be scanned, copied or duplicated, or posted to a publicly accessible website, in whole or in part.

CHAPTER 4

Medical Terminology

LEARNING OBJECTIVES

Studying and applying the material in this chapter will help you to:

- Understand the importance of being able to write, read, and communicate using medical terminology.

- Identify common roots and combining forms, suffixes, and prefixes.

- Break down medical terms into their component parts and interpret the terms correctly.

- Use the spelling and pronunciation guidelines for medical terms derived from Greek and Latin.

- Define common abbreviations and interpret common symbols.

- Evaluate the features of a medical dictionary to determine its value as a reference for your specialty area.

- Approach the learning of medical terminology by using a variety of study techniques.

© 2012 Cengage Learning. All Rights Reserved. May not be scanned, copied or duplicated, or posted to a publicly accessible website, in whole or in part.

VOCABULARY REVIEW

Definitions

Write the definition of each of the following words or terms.

1. combining form

   _____

   _____

   _____

2. combining vowel

   _____

   _____

   _____

3. consonant

   _____

   _____

   _____

4. medical terminology

   _____

   _____

   _____

5. prefix

   _____

   _____

   _____

6. suffix

   _____

   _____

   _____

7. word part

   _____

   _____

   _____

8. word root

   _____

   _____

   _____

© 2012 Cengage Learning. All Rights Reserved. May not be scanned, copied or duplicated, or posted to a publicly accessible website, in whole or in part.

Matching

Match the following combining forms with their their correct meanings.

____ 1. cephal/o	A. head
____ 2. cost/o	B. rib
____ 3. cyt/o	C. cell
____ 4. cyst/o	D. gallbladder
____ 5. myel/o	E. blood
____ 6. pharyng/o	F. muscle
____ 7. oste/o	G. spinal cord
____ 8. my/o	H. urinary bladder
____ 9. hem/o	I. bone
____ 10. cholecyst/o	J. throat

CHAPTER REVIEW

Identification

Place an "X" in front of each letter that may be used as a combining vowel.

____ 1. a

____ 2. c

____ 3. g

____ 4. i

____ 5. e

____ 6. o

____ 7. y

____ 8. u

____ 9. x

____ 10. m

True/False

Indicate whether the following statements are true (T) or false (F).

____ 1. Hepat/o is a suffix.

____ 2. Phleb/o means vein.

© 2012 Cengage Learning. All Rights Reserved. May not be scanned, copied or duplicated, or posted to a publicly accessible website, in whole or in part.

_____ 3. Cardiomegaly means a smaller than normal sized heart.

_____ 4. Medical terminology should be used when communicating with patients to ensure accurate communications.

_____ 5. Suffixes are word parts that are attached to the end of word roots and combining forms to add to or change their meaning.

_____ 6. Prefixes are word parts that are attached to the beginning of word roots and combining forms to add to or change their meaning.

_____ 7. When deciphering medical terms it is best to work from the word root, then prefix, and lastly the suffix.

_____ 8. Adip/o, lip/o, and steat/o are all combining forms that mean fat.

_____ 9. Bucco/o is a combining form that means intestine.

_____ 10. Lumpectomy means an incision into a lump.

Multiple Choice

Circle the best answer for each of the following questions. There is only one correct answer to each question.

1. Which of the following combining forms means armpit?

    A. arthr/o
    B. adip/o
    C. axill/o

2. Which of the following parts of a medical term gives the word its main meaning?

    A. root
    B. suffix
    C. prefix

3. Which of the following word roots means stomach?

    A. enter
    B. cardi
    C. gastr

4. Which of the following suffixes means pain?

    A. cide
    B. centesis
    C. algia

5. Which of the following words means a record of the electrical activity of the heart?

    A. electrocardiograph
    B. electrocardiogram
    C. electrocardiography

© 2012 Cengage Learning. All Rights Reserved. May not be scanned, copied or duplicated, or posted to a publicly accessible website, in whole or in part.

6. Which of the following descriptions best describes hemiplegia?

    A. numbness of the entire body
    B. burning sensation of the body
    C. paralysis of one side (half) of the body

7. Which of the following prefixes means against?

    A. anti
    B. auto
    C. dys

8. Which of the following prefixes means after or behind?

    A. post
    B. pre
    C. sub

9. Which of the following abbreviations means twice a day?

    A. a.c.
    B. b.i.d
    C. t.i.d

10. If a patient has an order for n.p.o. and his or her breakfast tray arrives, what is the most appropriate action?

    A. Take the breakfast tray to the patient's room.
    B. Do not take the breakfast tray to the patient's room.
    C. Remove the items that are not liquid and then take it to the patient's room.

Short Answer

Read each question. Think about the information presented in the text, and then answer each question.

1. When pronouncing the words *cell, circulatory,* and *cyst* the *c* sounds like *s*. What medical spelling and pronunciation guideline does this refer to?

    _____

    _____

    _____

2. When pronouncing the word *chronic* the *ch* sounds like *k*. What medical spelling and pronunciation guideline does this refer to?

    _____

    _____

    _____

© 2012 Cengage Learning. All Rights Reserved. May not be scanned, copied or duplicated, or posted to a publicly accessible website, in whole or in part.

3. Define difference between *gastr* and *gastr/o.*

   _____

   _____

   _____

4. Describe the difference between appendicitis and appendectomy.

   _____

   _____

   _____

5. How is the plural usually formed when the term ends in *is*?

   _____

   _____

   _____

6. What is the recommended procedure to follow when deciphering medical terms?

   _____

   _____

   _____

7. Using medical abbreviations, write that a patient should have his or her vital signs taken four times a day and can be up walking freely, at will and without assistance.

   _____

   _____

   _____

8. If a patient is to be given a medication *p.c.*, when would you administer the medication?

   _____

   _____

   _____

9. Explain the difference between *ASAP* and *stat*. Which is the most urgent?

   _____

   _____

   _____

10. The plural for *ganglion* is *ganglia*. Write the guideline to making plural forms that this follows.

    _____

    _____

    _____

© 2012 Cengage Learning. All Rights Reserved. May not be scanned, copied or duplicated, or posted to a publicly accessible website, in whole or in part.

Completion

Use the words in the list to complete the following statements.

arteri/o	ven/o or phleb/o	derm/o or dermat/o	viv/o
lapar/o	ren/o or nephr/o	laryng/o	cide
emia	otomy		

1. A combining form that means vein is _____.

2. A combining form that means artery is _____.

3. A combining form that means life is _____.

4. A combining form that means abdominal wall is _____.

5. A combining form that means voice box or larynx is _____.

6. A combining form that means kidneys is _____.

7. A combining form that means skin is _____.

8. A suffix that means to kill or destroy is _____.

9. A suffix that means surgical incision is _____.

10. A suffix that means blood is _____.

Critical Thinking Scenarios

Read each scenario. Think about the information presented in the text, and then answer each question.

1. Janet, age 45, has been feeling unusually tired and has noted an unexplained weight gain. She goes to her provider, who determines she has hypothyroidism.

   A. What does hypothyroidism mean?

   _____

   _____

   _____

   B. What does hyperthyroidism mean?

   _____

   _____

   _____

© 2012 Cengage Learning. All Rights Reserved. May not be scanned, copied or duplicated, or posted to a publicly accessible website, in whole or in part.

2. Bob, age 56, was seen by his provider for intestinal problems. When he arrived home, he decided to research a word his provider used which sounded like "ILL ee um."

   A. There are two medical terms that are pronounced "ILL ee um." What are they?

   _____

   _____

   _____

   B. What does each term mean?

   _____

   _____

   _____

   C. Which term was the most likely one the provider was using?

   _____

   _____

   _____

© 2012 Cengage Learning. All Rights Reserved. May not be scanned, copied or duplicated, or posted to a publicly accessible website, in whole or in part.

CHAPTER 5

Medical Math

LEARNING OBJECTIVES

Studying and applying the material in this chapter will help you to:

- Understand how math anxiety prevents comfort and competence with calculations.
- Perform basic math calculations on whole numbers, decimals, fractions, percentages, and ratios.
- Convert between the following numerical forms: decimals, fractions, percentages, and ratios.
- Round off numbers correctly.
- Solve mathematical equivalency problems with proportions.
- Express time using the 24-hour clock (military time).
- Express numbers using Roman numerals.
- Estimate angles from a reference plane.
- Use household, metric, and apothecary units to express length, volume, and weight.
- Know equivalencies for converting between the household, metric, and apothecary systems of measurement.
- Convert between the Fahrenheit and Celsius temperature scales.

© 2012 Cengage Learning. All Rights Reserved. May not be scanned, copied or duplicated, or posted to a publicly accessible website, in whole or in part.

VOCABULARY REVIEW

Matching

Match the following terms with their correct definitions.

_____ 1. metric system

    A. a method of telling time that is based on a 24-hour clock.

_____ 2. military time

    B. a method used to express a whole or part of a whole. The whole is written as 100%.

_____ 3. nomenclature

    C. a method used to express the strength of a solution; it represents how many parts of one element are added in relationship to the parts of another element.

_____ 4. percentages

    D. a numbering system based on I (1), V (5), X (10), L (50), C (100), D (500), and M (1000).

_____ 5. proportion

    E. a mathematical statement of equality between two ratios.

_____ 6. ratio

    F. method of naming.

_____ 7. reciprocal

    G. a real or imaginary flat surface from which an angle is measured.

_____ 8. reference plane

    H. rules that determine whether a number is changed to zero, increased, or remains the same when digits are dropped from the right side.

_____ 9. Roman numerals

    I. the traditional numbers we use to count (1, 2, 3...).

_____ 10. rounding numbers

    J. a measurement system based on 10s; basic units are length (meter), volume (liter), and weight (gram).

_____ 11. whole numbers

    K. a fraction that has been "turned upside down" during the process of dividing fractions.

Word Fill

Complete the following sentences by filling in the missing words.

angles	apothecary system	centigrade (C) scale	decimal system
degrees	estimating	Fahrenheit (F) scale	fraction
household system	improper fraction	math anxiety	

1. The _____ is a measurement system that is used infrequently except for a measurement of weight (grain).

2. _____ are units of measurement used in angles, temperature readings, and depth of burns.

© 2012 Cengage Learning. All Rights Reserved. May not be scanned, copied or duplicated, or posted to a publicly accessible website, in whole or in part.

3. The _____ is a linear arrangement of numbers based on units of 10, containing a point to separate the whole number from the fractional part of a number (e.g., 2.5).

4. The _____ is a method used to express numbers that are not whole numbers; it has a numerator and a denominator.

5. The _____ is a measurement system based on common household items used to measure length, volume, and weight.

6. _____ are the amount of variance from a reference plane expressed in degrees.

7. _____ is a measurement of temperature based on a freezing point of 32° and a boiling point of 212°.

8. A/An _____ is a fraction that has a numerator that is larger than the denominator.

9. _____ is expressing the approximate answer.

10. _____ is a strong negative reaction to math that interferes with the ability to concentrate, learn, and perform math calculations.

11. _____ is a measurement of temperature based on a freezing point of 0° and a boiling point of 100°.

CHAPTER REVIEW

Identification

Place an "X" in front of the following activities that might require math calculations.

_____ 1. administering medications

_____ 2. recording height and weight

_____ 3. tracking intake and output

_____ 4. billing tasks

_____ 5. performing lab tests

_____ 6. mixing solutions

_____ 7. assisting in surgery

_____ 8. providing therapeutic services

_____ 9. taking vital signs

_____ 10. documenting in a patient's chart

© 2012 Cengage Learning. All Rights Reserved. May not be scanned, copied or duplicated, or posted to a publicly accessible website, in whole or in part.

True/False

Indicate whether the following statements are true (T) or false (F).

_____ 1. Work in health care requires the use of math skills to measure and perform various types of calculations.

_____ 2. Dividing fractions requires the dividing fraction to be inverted (turned upside down). The new, upside-down fraction is called an improper fraction.

_____ 3. Rounding 135 to the nearest whole number would be 135.

_____ 4. Rounding 274.56 to the nearest whole number would be 275.

_____ 5. The military time of 1230 would be expressed as 12:30 a.m. in traditional time.

_____ 6. The Roman numeral XXVIII is 27 in Arabic numbers.

_____ 7. A needle held perpendicular to the reference plane would be at a 180 degree angle.

_____ 8. In the household measurement system there are three teaspoons in one tablespoon.

_____ 9. To convert grams to kilograms, you would add three zeros.

_____ 10. To convert grams to centigrams, you would add three zeros.

Multiple Choice

Circle the best answer for each of the following questions. There is only one correct answer to each question.

1. Which of the following is true about math anxiety?

    A. it is a learned behavior
    B. it is an inherited trait
    C. it cannot be overcome

2. How is 1.60 read?

    A. one and sixty-tenths
    B. one and six-tenths
    C. one and sixty-hundredths

3. Which is the proper way to write three milligrams?

    A. 3.0 mg
    B. 0.3 mg
    C. 3 mg

4. Which of the following abbreviations is acceptable to use in medical documentation?

    A. U
    B. mL
    C. cc

© 2012 Cengage Learning. All Rights Reserved. May not be scanned, copied or duplicated, or posted to a publicly accessible website, in whole or in part.

5. What is the result of multiplying 1.5 times 1.125?

   A. 0.16875
   B. 168.75
   C. 1.6875

6. What is the result of adding 1/2 to 1/3?

   A. 2/5
   B. 5/6
   C. 1/6

7. What would the decimal 0.75 be converted to when expressed as a fraction?

   A. 3/4
   B. 75%
   C. 7.5

8. What is the military time for 4 p.m.?

   A. 0400
   B. 0160
   C. 1600

9. How many ounces are in one cup?

   A. 4
   B. 8
   C. 16

10. A child measures 19 inches in length. How many centimeters is this?

   A. 47.5
   B. 7.6
   C. 38

Short Answer

Read each question. Think about the information presented in the text, and then answer each question.

1. Why is it critical that health care workers strive for 100% accuracy in math?

   _____

   _____

   _____

2. What is math anxiety? Can it be overcome?

   _____

   _____

   _____

© 2012 Cengage Learning. All Rights Reserved. May not be scanned, copied or duplicated, or posted to a publicly accessible website, in whole or in part.

3. What is the number 345.345 rounded to the nearest tens and the nearest tenths?

_____

_____

_____

4. If a patient is 66 inches tall, how would that be expressed in feet?

_____

_____

_____

5. What is the value of estimating in calculations?

_____

_____

_____

6. What are the seven key numerals used with Roman numerals and what value does each represent?

_____

_____

_____

7. What is the nomenclature in the metric system for distance/length, capacity/volume, and mass/weight?

_____

_____

_____

8. What do the prefixes *kilo, centi,* and *milli* mean?   •

_____

_____

_____

9. What are the primary approximate equivalents between measuring systems?

_____

_____

_____

10. How do the boiling and freezing points between the Fahrenheit (F) and Celsius (C) systems compare?

_____

_____

_____

© 2012 Cengage Learning. All Rights Reserved. May not be scanned, copied or duplicated, or posted to a publicly accessible website, in whole or in part.

Critical Thinking Scenarios

Read each scenario. Think about the information presented in the text, and then answer each question.

1. Mr. John Brown says he has medication that states he is to take 15 milliliters every day. He is confused by the instructions and asks you to clarify.

   A. How many milliliters are in 1 teaspoon?

   _____

   _____

   _____

   B. How many milliliters are in 1 tablespoon?

   _____

   _____

   _____

   C. What amount would you recommend for him to take?

   _____

   _____

   _____

2. A patient states that she weighs 125 pounds and wants to know how that converts to kilograms.

   A. What is the equivalent between the two systems?

   _____

   _____

   _____

   B. What are the abbreviations for pounds and kilograms?

   _____

   _____

   _____

   C. How much does the patient weigh in kilograms rounded to the nearest tenth?

   _____

   _____

   _____

© 2012 Cengage Learning. All Rights Reserved. May not be scanned, copied or duplicated, or posted to a publicly accessible website, in whole or in part.

UNIT 3
The Human Body

© 2012 Cengage Learning. All Rights Reserved. May not be scanned, copied or duplicated, or posted to a publicly accessible website, in whole or in part.

CHAPTER 6

Organization of the Human Body

LEARNING OBJECTIVES

Studying and applying the material in this chapter will help you to:

- Explain the meaning of homeostasis.
- Name the levels in the structural organization of the body.
- Name and explain the function of the main cellular components.
- Name and describe the four primary types of tissues.
- Describe the anatomical position.
- Identify and describe the location of the three directional body planes.
- Use directional terms to describe various locations on the body.
- Name the main body cavities and what structures are found in each.
- Identify the abdominal regions and quadrants.

© 2012 Cengage Learning. All Rights Reserved. May not be scanned, copied or duplicated, or posted to a publicly accessible website, in whole or in part.

VOCABULARY REVIEW

Matching 1

Match the following terms with their correct definitions.

_____ 1. lateral

_____ 2. medial

_____ 3. midsagittal plane

_____ 4. organ

_____ 5. pelvic cavity

_____ 6. peripheral

_____ 7. posterior (dorsal)

_____ 8. posterior body cavity

_____ 9. proximal

_____ 10. spinal cavity

_____ 11. superficial

_____ 12. superior

_____ 13. tissue

_____ 14. thoracic cavity

_____ 15. transverse plane

A. away from the center of the body (toward the sides)

B. anatomical term meaning away from the center

C. located in the chest; contains the heart, lungs, and major blood vessels

D. passes through the midline and divides the body vertically into equal right and left portions

E. groups of cells with a similar function

F. consists of the cranial and spinal cavity; protects the structures of the nervous system; also called dorsal body cavity

G. near or close to the body surface

H. toward the midline or center of body

I. divides the body horizontally into top and bottom portions

J. located within the spinal column; contains the spinal cord

K. above

L. located in the lower abdomen; contains the urinary bladder, rectum, and reproductive organs

M. closer to the reference point

N. toward the back of the body

O. the combination of two or more types of tissues that work together to perform a specific body function

© 2012 Cengage Learning. All Rights Reserved. May not be scanned, copied or duplicated, or posted to a publicly accessible website, in whole or in part.

Word Fill

Complete the following sentences by filling in the missing words.

abdominal cavity	anatomical position	anterior (ventral)	anterior body cavity
apex	base	body system	caudal
cell	cephalic (cranial)	cranial cavity	deep
distal	frontal plane	homeostasis	inferior

1. _____ is at the top (highest point).

2. _____ is closer to the coccyx (lower back).

3. _____ is the tendency of a cell or the whole organism to maintain a state of balance.

4. _____ is when the body as viewed in a full upright position (standing), with the arms relaxed at the sides of the body, palms facing forward, feet pointed forward, and the eyes directed straight ahead.

5. A _____ is a combination of two or more organs to provide a major body function.

6. _____ is farther from the reference base point.

7. The _____ divides the body vertically into front and back portions.

8. _____ is at the bottom (lowest point).

9. The _____ contains the stomach, intestines, liver, gallbladder, pancreas, and spleen.

10. _____ means farther from the body surface.

11. The _____ is located in the skull; it contains the brain.

12. The _____ consists of the thoracic, abdominal, and pelvic cavities; protects the internal organs; also called ventral body cavity.

13. A _____ is the smallest living structure of the body.

14. _____ is closer to the head.

15. _____ is below.

16. _____ is toward the front of body.

CHAPTER REVIEW

Identification

Place an "X" in front of the cell components that are organelles.

_____ 1. endoplasmic reticulum

_____ 2. centrioles

© 2012 Cengage Learning. All Rights Reserved. May not be scanned, copied or duplicated, or posted to a publicly accessible website, in whole or in part.

_____ 3. cell membrane

_____ 4. nucleus

_____ 5. cytoplasm

_____ 6. vacuole

_____ 7. protoplasm

_____ 8. golgi apparatus

_____ 9. ribosomes

_____ 10. lysosome

_____ 11. mitochondrion

True/False

Indicate whether the following statements are true (T) or false (F).

_____ 1. Adjustments made to maintain homeostasis occur without our conscious awareness.

_____ 2. The posterior (dorsal) cavity includes the thoracic, abdominal, and pelvic cavities.

_____ 3. The nucleus controls the activity of the cell.

_____ 4. The umbilicus is on the anterior surface of the body.

_____ 5. When standing in the anatomical position, the elbows are on the posterior (dorsal) side of the body.

_____ 6. The elbow is proximal to the shoulder.

_____ 7. The breasts are caudal to the waist.

_____ 8. In the anatomical position, the thumb is medial to the other fingers.

_____ 9. An abrasion below the armpit would be on the lateral side of the body.

_____ 10. The epigastric region is located superior to the hypogastric region.

Matching 2

Match the following types of cells with their correct functions. Each function is used only once.

_____ 1. bone cells   A. communication

_____ 2. nerve cells   B. protection

_____ 3. skin cells   C. oxygen transportation

_____ 4. muscle cells   D. movement

_____ 5. red blood cells   E. support

© 2012 Cengage Learning. All Rights Reserved. May not be scanned, copied or duplicated, or posted to a publicly accessible website, in whole or in part.

Ordering

Place the following structures in the order of the smallest to the largest level. Put a numeral 1 before the smallest structure, a 2 before the next, and so on.

_____ 1. organs

_____ 2. tissues

_____ 3. human body as a whole

_____ 4. cell

_____ 5. body (organ) systems

Labeling

Assign the major components of the cell from the list below to the appropriate places on the figure.

Figure 6-1

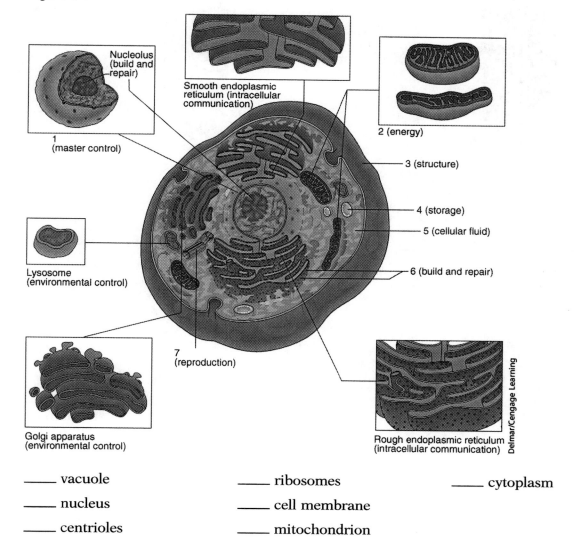

_____ vacuole   _____ ribosomes   _____ cytoplasm

_____ nucleus   _____ cell membrane   _____ mitochondrion

_____ centrioles   _____ mitochondrion

© 2012 Cengage Learning. All Rights Reserved. May not be scanned, copied or duplicated, or posted to a publicly accessible website, in whole or in part.

Assign the directional terms from the following list to the appropriate places on the figures.

Figure 6-2a and 6-2b

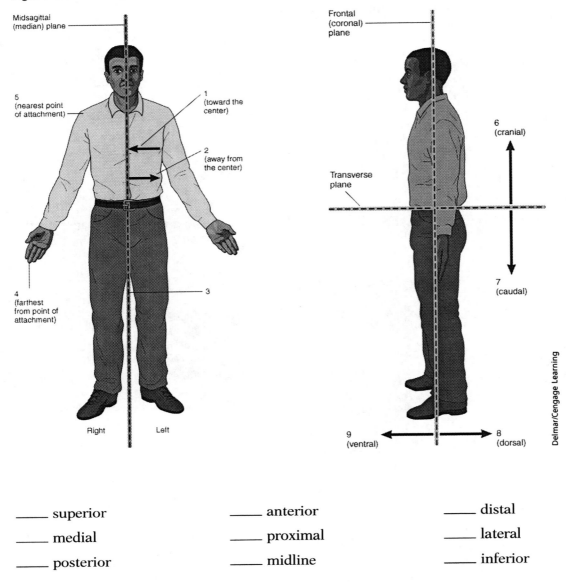

_____ superior   _____ anterior   _____ distal

_____ medial   _____ proximal   _____ lateral

_____ posterior   _____ midline   _____ inferior

© 2012 Cengage Learning. All Rights Reserved. May not be scanned, copied or duplicated, or posted to a publicly accessible website, in whole or in part.

Assign the body cavities from the following list to the appropriate places on the figure.

Figure 6-3

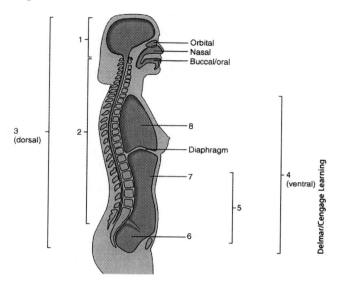

_____ posterior   _____ anterior   _____ abdominal

_____ abdominopelvic   _____ spinal   _____ pelvic

_____ thoracic   _____ cranial

Assign the labels from the following list to the appropriate places on the figures.

Figure 6-4a and 6-4b

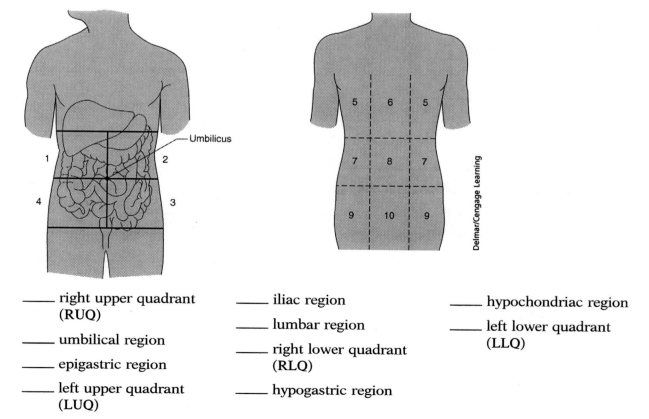

_____ right upper quadrant (RUQ)

_____ umbilical region

_____ epigastric region

_____ left upper quadrant (LUQ)

_____ iliac region

_____ lumbar region

_____ right lower quadrant (RLQ)

_____ hypogastric region

_____ hypochondriac region

_____ left lower quadrant (LLQ)

© 2012 Cengage Learning. All Rights Reserved. May not be scanned, copied or duplicated, or posted to a publicly accessible website, in whole or in part.

Critical Thinking Scenarios

Read each scenario. Think about the information presented in the text, and then answer each question.

1. Mr. Travis Weathers arrives in the emergency room with complaints of severe abdominal pain after an accident. When asks where the pain is he rubs his hand clear across the abdomen above the umbilicus.

    A. Using the four quadrant model, how would you describe this location?

    _____

    _____

    _____

    B. Is the pain on the anterior (ventral) or posterior (dorsal) side of the body?

    _____

    _____

    _____

    C. Would lateral or medial be used in this description?

    _____

    _____

    _____

2. Ms. Matilda Bush is taken to surgery after sustaining multiple abrasions from a motorcycle accident. It is necessary to anesthetize her in order to remove the gravel that has been ground into her skin. She also has a bruised area that extends from the shoulder to the elbow of the left arm. You also note there is moderate edema of her feet and ankles.

    A. Would her injuries be considered superficial or deep?

    _____

    _____

    _____

    B. How would you describe the location of the bruise?

    _____

    _____

    _____

    C. How would you describe the edema?

    _____

    _____

    _____

•

© 2012 Cengage Learning. All Rights Reserved. May not be scanned, copied or duplicated, or posted to a publicly accessible website, in whole or in part.

CHAPTER 7

Structure and Function of the Human Body

LEARNING OBJECTIVES

Studying and applying the material in this chapter will help you to:

- Understand and explain the difference between anatomy, physiology, and pathophysiology.

- Define what determines a state of wellness as opposed to illness.

- Describe the primary anatomical features and physiological actions of the systems for movement and protection of the body.

- Name and demonstrate the movements made possible by joints.

- Describe the primary anatomical features and physiological actions of the systems for providing energy and for removing waste from the body.

- Describe the primary anatomical features and physiological actions of the systems for sensing and for coordinating and controlling the body.

- Describe the primary anatomical features and physiological actions of the systems for producing new life.

- Name common diseases or disorders associated with each system.

- Describe the behaviors and actions for each body system that promote health and prevent major diseases and disorders.

© 2012 Cengage Learning. All Rights Reserved. May not be scanned, copied or duplicated, or posted to a publicly accessible website, in whole or in part.

VOCABULARY REVIEW

Definitions

Write the definition of each of the following words or terms.

1. anatomy

_____

_____

_____

2. diagnosis

_____

_____

_____

3. diagnostic procedures

_____

_____

_____

4. diseases

_____

_____

_____

5. etiology

_____

_____

_____

6. illness

_____

_____

_____

7. objective

_____

_____

_____

8. pathophysiology

_____

_____

_____

© 2012 Cengage Learning. All Rights Reserved. May not be scanned, copied or duplicated, or posted to a publicly accessible website, in whole or in part.

Matching 1

Match the following terms with their correct definitions.

——— 1. physiology

A. promotion of health through preventive measures and the practice of good health habits; when the body is in a state of homeostasis

——— 2. prevention (of disease)

B. information the patient tells the health care worker about his or her condition that cannot be directly observed

——— 3. prognosis

C. prediction of the possible outcome of a disease and the potential for recovery

——— 4. signs and symptoms

D. medications or procedures used to control or cure a disease or injury

——— 5. subjective

E. not a precise disease but a group of related signs and symptoms

——— 6. syndrome

F. the objective evidence observed by the health care worker and the subjective data reported by patients about their condition

——— 7. wellness

G. the study of the functions (how and why something works) of an organism

——— 8. treatment

H. behaviors that promote health and prevent disease

CHAPTER REVIEW

Identification

Place an "X" in front of the bones that are part of the axial skeleton.

——— 1. hyoid

——— 2. feet

——— 3. skull

——— 4. inner ear

——— 5. pelvis

——— 6. hands

——— 7. spinal column

——— 8. legs

——— 9. arms

——— 10. ribs

——— 11. sternum

© 2012 Cengage Learning. All Rights Reserved. May not be scanned, copied or duplicated, or posted to a publicly accessible website, in whole or in part.

True/False Rewrite

Please rewrite the bold part of the sentence to make the statement true.

1. The **atrioventricular node (AV node)** is known as the natural pacemaker of the heart.

   _____

   _____

   _____

2. The **dermis** is the outer layer of the skin.

   _____

   _____

   _____

3. **Platelets** are the liquid part of the blood, consisting mostly of water.

   _____

   _____

   _____

4. The second essential transportation system of the body is the **endocrine** system.

   _____

   _____

   _____

5. **Leukemia** results when the blood has an inadequate amount of hemoglobin, red blood cells, or both.

   _____

   _____

   _____

6. The **nervous** system provides energy for the body by processing food.

   _____

   _____

   _____

7. **An ulcer** is a condition in which the lining of the abdominal cavity becomes inflamed.

   _____

   _____

   _____

8. **Edema** is a disease.

   _____

   _____

   _____

© 2012 Cengage Learning. All Rights Reserved. May not be scanned, copied or duplicated, or posted to a publicly accessible website, in whole or in part.

9. The **conjunctiva** produce tears for cleaning and moisturizing the eyes.

_____

_____

_____

10. The **cochlea** are three tiny, delicate bones that form a chain to carry and amplify sound vibrations from the eardrum.

_____

_____

_____

Multiple Choice

Circle the best answer for each of the following questions. There is only one correct answer to each question.

1. Which of the following is a lateral curvature of the spine?

   A. kyphosis
   B. lordosis
   C. scoliosis

2. Which of the following is an inward curvature of the lumbar area?

   A. kyphosis
   B. lordosis
   C. scoliosis

3. Which of the following is a rounded bowing of the thoracic area?

   A. kyphosis
   B. lordosis
   C. scoliosis

4. Which of the following is the medical term for the throat?

   A. larynx
   B. pharynx
   C. trachea

5. Which of the following structures have villi?

   A. throat
   B. stomach
   C. small intestine

6. Which of the following is also known as myopia?

   A. nearsightedness
   B. farsightedness
   C. glaucoma

© 2012 Cengage Learning. All Rights Reserved. May not be scanned, copied or duplicated, or posted to a publicly accessible website, in whole or in part.

7. Which of the following is part of the peripheral nervous system?

   A. brain
   B. spinal cord
   C. cranial nerves

8. Which of the following conditions is caused by excessive thyroid hormones?

   A. hyperthyroidism
   B. hypothyroidism
   C. acromegaly

9. Which of the following structures connects the bladder to the exterior of the body?

   A. ureter
   B. urethra
   C. uvula

10. Which of the following is an inflammation of the testes?

    A. phimosis
    B. epididymitis
    C. orchitis

Matching 2

Match the following terms with their correct definitions.

_____ 1. phimosis	A. tumors of the uterus
_____ 2. dementia	B. excessive hormone production of the adrenal cortex
_____ 3. encephalitis	C. tightness of the foreskin over the end of the penis
_____ 4. macular degeneration	D. abnormal electrical impulses in the neurons
_____ 5. glaucoma	E. infection of the middle ear
_____ 6. diabetes mellitus	F. loss of memory and impairment of mental function
_____ 7. otitis media	G. infection of the brain
_____ 8. Cushing's syndrome	H. increased pressure in the eye
_____ 9. epilepsy	I. disorder of the retina
_____ 10. fibroid tumors	J. caused by inadequate insulin

© 2012 Cengage Learning. All Rights Reserved. May not be scanned, copied or duplicated, or posted to a publicly accessible website, in whole or in part.

Completion

Use the words in the list to complete the following statements:

flat	short	periosteum	medullary canal
irregular	red marrow	cartilage	long
diaphysis	epiphyses		

1. The _____ is the center cavity of a long bone containing yellow marrow.

2. The _____ is the portion that runs between the ends of the bone.

3. The _____ are the ends of the bone (proximal and distal).

4. The _____ is the white, fibrous layer that covers the outside of bone; contains blood, lymph vessels, and nerves.

5. The _____ is the part of the bone that manufactures the red blood cells (RBCs), which carry oxygen, and the white blood cells (WBCs), which protect the body from infections.

6. The _____ is the elastic connective tissue that covers the end of the bones and functions as a cushion between bones.

7. _____ bones are longer than they are wide (e.g., humerus, femur, fingers and toes).

8. _____ bones are similar in length and width (e.g., carpals and tarsals).

9. _____ bones have two layers with space between them (e.g., cranium, ribs, and pelvis).

10. _____ bones are those that do not fit into any other category (e.g., vertebrae and patella).

Ordering 1

Place the following list of electrical structures and cardiac responses in the order in which they would occur. Put a numeral 1 before the structure where the electrical impulse originates, a 2 before the next, and so on.

_____ 1. left and right atria contract

_____ 2. bundle of His

_____ 3. atrioventricular node (AV node)

_____ 4. sinoatrial node (SA node)

_____ 5. right and left bundle fibers

_____ 6. right and left ventricles contract

_____ 7. Purkinje fibers

© 2012 Cengage Learning. All Rights Reserved. May not be scanned, copied or duplicated, or posted to a publicly accessible website, in whole or in part.

Ordering 2

Place the following list in the proper sequence to represent the flow of the blood through the cardiovascular system. Put a numeral 1 before the structures that bring the blood from the body to the heart, 2 before the next, and so on.

_____ 1. right atrium

_____ 2. left ventricle

_____ 3. superior and inferior vena cavae

_____ 4. pulmonary veins

_____ 5. left atrium

_____ 6. pulmonary arteries

_____ 7. right ventricle

_____ 8. lungs

_____ 9. aorta

Labeling

Assign the labels from the list below to the appropriate places on the figure.

Figure 7-1

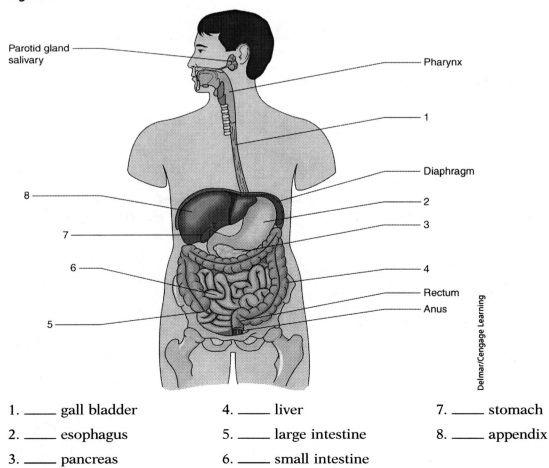

1. _____ gall bladder   4. _____ liver   7. _____ stomach

2. _____ esophagus   5. _____ large intestine   8. _____ appendix

3. _____ pancreas   6. _____ small intestine

© 2012 Cengage Learning. All Rights Reserved. May not be scanned, copied or duplicated, or posted to a publicly accessible website, in whole or in part.

Assign the labels from the list below to the appropriate places on the figure.

Figure 7-2

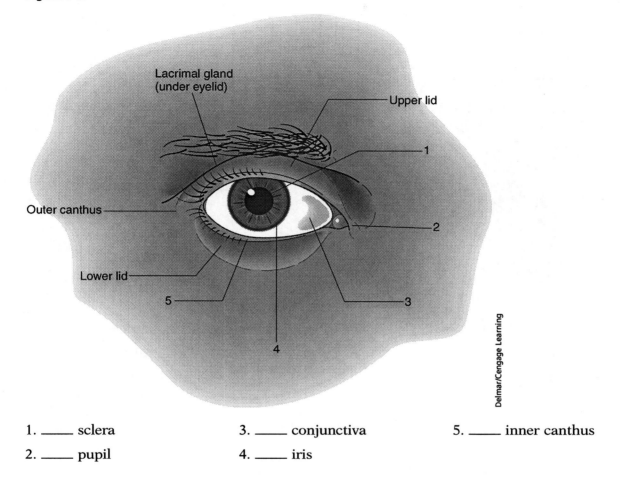

1. _____ sclera   3. _____ conjunctiva   5. _____ inner canthus
2. _____ pupil   4. _____ iris

© 2012 Cengage Learning. All Rights Reserved. May not be scanned, copied or duplicated, or posted to a publicly accessible website, in whole or in part.

Assign the labels from the list below to the appropriate places on the figure.

Figure 7-3

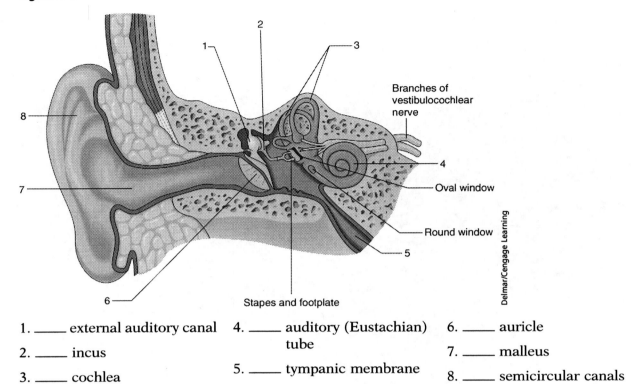

1. _____ external auditory canal

2. _____ incus

3. _____ cochlea

4. _____ auditory (Eustachian) tube

5. _____ tympanic membrane

6. _____ auricle

7. _____ malleus

8. _____ semicircular canals

© 2012 Cengage Learning. All Rights Reserved. May not be scanned, copied or duplicated, or posted to a publicly accessible website, in whole or in part.

Assign the labels from the list below to the appropriate places on the figure.

Figure 7-4

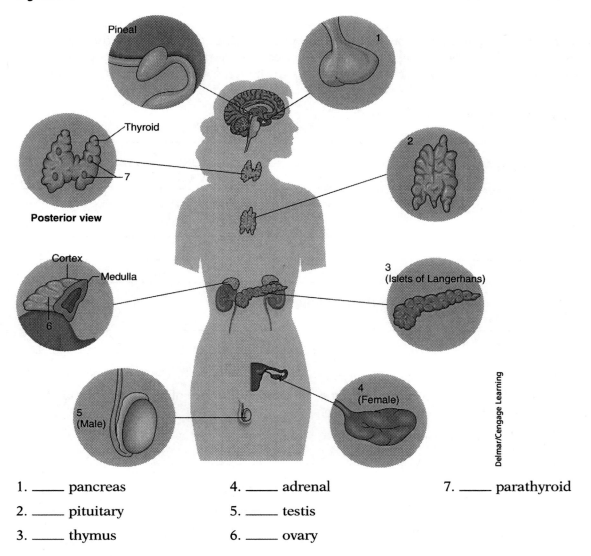

1. _____ pancreas   4. _____ adrenal   7. _____ parathyroid

2. _____ pituitary   5. _____ testis

3. _____ thymus   6. _____ ovary

© 2012 Cengage Learning. All Rights Reserved. May not be scanned, copied or duplicated, or posted to a publicly accessible website, in whole or in part.

Critical Thinking Scenarios

Read each scenario. Think about the information presented in the text, and then answer each question.

1. Juanita Barber thought she was just having a chest cold, but when she started to have increasing difficulty breathing she went to the health care provider. She has a chest X-ray done and is informed there is atelectasis in the left lower lobe and the diagnosis is pneumonia.

    A. What is atelectasis and what is the likely cause?

    _____

    _____

    _____

    B. What causes pneumonia?

    _____

    _____

    _____

    C. How many lobes are there in the two lungs?

    _____

    _____

    _____

2. Lam Pham has not been feeling well for some time. A number of tests were run and it was determined he has Hodgkin's disease.

    A. What is Hodgkin's disease?

    _____

    _____

    _____

    B. What system does this disease involve?

    _____

    _____

    _____

    C. What is the function of this system?

    _____

    _____

    _____

© 2012 Cengage Learning. All Rights Reserved. May not be scanned, copied or duplicated, or posted to a publicly accessible website, in whole or in part.

CHAPTER 8

Growth and Development

LEARNING OBJECTIVES

Studying and applying the material in this chapter will help you to:

- Explain the difference between "physical," "cognitive," and "psychosocial" as they relate to growth and development.
- Identify the nine life stages and the corresponding age span for each.
- Discuss the physical, cognitive, and psychosocial changes that occur at each life stage.
- Identify the psychosocial developmental tasks to be accomplished according to the theory of Erik Erikson.
- Implement specific approaches to care at each life stage based on a knowledge of growth and development.
- Identify and describe the five stages of the dying process.

VOCABULARY

Definitions

Write the definition of each of the following words or terms.

1. chronic illness

   _____

   _____

   _____

2. cognitive

   _____

   _____

   _____

© 2012 Cengage Learning. All Rights Reserved. May not be scanned, copied or duplicated, or posted to a publicly accessible website, in whole or in part.

3. development

_____   •   _____

_____

_____

4. growth

_____

_____

_____

Word Fill

Complete the following sentences by filling in the missing words.

Erikson's stages   life review   physical development   psychosocial
of psychosocial   stages of dying
development   terminal illness

1. _____ is a theory based on the psychosocial challenges that are
   presented to individuals as they progress through life stages.

2. _____ is an illness from which the patient is expected to die because
   there is no known cure.

3. _____ is the growth of the body, including motor sensory adaptation.

4. _____ is the telling the events of one's life as a form of self-evaluation
   and closure as the end of life approaches.

5. The _____ are the stages that dying persons may experience as they
   face the fact of their own death. The five stages are denial, anger, bargaining, depression,
   and acceptance.

6. _____ refers to the emotions, attitudes, and other aspects of the mind,
   in addition to the individual's interactions and relationships with other members of
   society.

© 2012 Cengage Learning. All Rights Reserved. May not be scanned, copied or duplicated, or posted to a publicly accessible website, in whole or in part.

CHAPTER REVIEW

Identification 1

Place an "X" in front of the care considerations appropriate to the infancy life stage.

_____ 1. involve parents in care

_____ 2. use a firm, direct approach

_____ 3. set limits and maintain safety

_____ 4. praise good behavior

_____ 5. cuddle and hug

Identification 2

Place an "X" in front of the care considerations appropriate to the toddler life stage.

_____ 1. set limits and maintain safety

_____ 2. distract and use a game approach to improve cooperation

_____ 3. use a firm, direct approach

_____ 4. give only one direction at a time and state it simply

_____ 5. give explanations along with the rationale

Identification 3

Place an "X" in front of the care considerations appropriate to the adolescence life stage.

_____ 1. encourage questions

_____ 2. provide privacy

_____ 3. explore support systems

_____ 4. encourage active learning, thinking, and use of memory skills

_____ 5. don't talk about them where they can overhear the conversation

Identification 4

Place an "X" in front of the care considerations appropriate to the young adulthood life stage.

_____ 1. use a firm, direct approach

_____ 2. involve parents in care

_____ 3. involve them in the decision-making process

_____ 4. watch body language for clues regarding feelings

_____ 5. define and enforce behavior limits

© 2012 Cengage Learning. All Rights Reserved. May not be scanned, copied or duplicated, or posted to a publicly accessible website, in whole or in part.

Identification 5

Place an "X" in front of the care considerations appropriate to the later adulthood life stage.

_____ 1. assist with adjustment to new roles

_____ 2. encourage active learning, thinking, and use of memory skills

_____ 3. provide a lot of physical contact

_____ 4. use a firm, direct approach

_____ 5. give only one direction at a time and state it simply

Multiple Choice

Circle the best answer for each of the following questions. There is only one correct answer to each question.

1. What is the infancy age range as defined by Erik Erikson's Stages of Psychosocial Development?

   A. conception to birth
   B. birth to 1 year
   C. birth to 2 years

2. What is the toddler age range as defined by Erik Erikson's Stages of Psychosocial Development?

   A. 6 months to 2 years
   B. 2 to 3 years
   C. 1 to 3 years

3. What is the preschooler age range as defined by Erik Erikson's Stages of Psychosocial Development?

   A. 3 to 6 years
   B. 2 to 5 years
   C. 4 to 7 years

4. What is the school-age child age range as defined by Erik Erikson's Stages of Psychosocial Development?

   A. 7 to 18 years
   B. 6 to 10 years
   C. 6 to 12 years

5. What is the adolescence age range as defined by Erik Erikson's Stages of Psychosocial Development?

   A. 10 to 18 years
   B. 12 to 20 years
   C. 13 to 16 years

© 2012 Cengage Learning. All Rights Reserved. May not be scanned, copied or duplicated, or posted to a publicly accessible website, in whole or in part.

6. What is the young adulthood age range as defined by Erik Erikson's Stages of Psychosocial Development?

   A. 20s and 30s
   B. teens and 20s
   C. 18 to 25 years

7. What is the middle adulthood age range as defined by Erik Erikson's Stages of Psychosocial Development?

   A. 30s and 40s
   B. 40s and 50s
   C. 40 to 65 years

8. What is the later adulthood age range as defined by Erik Erikson's Stages of Psychosocial Development?

   A. over 55 years
   B. over 65 years
   C. over 75 years

9. Which of the following stages of death and dying is usually the first to be experienced?

   A. anger
   B. depression
   C. denial

10. Which of the following developed the stages of death and dying?

    A. Dr. William Thomas
    B. Erik Erikson
    C. Elisabeth Kübler-Ross

Matching

Match the following terms with their correct definitions.

_____ 1. infancy	A. generativity vs. stagnation
_____ 2. toddler	B. ego integrity vs. despair
_____ 3. preschooler	C. initiative vs. guilt
_____ 4. school-age child	D. trust vs. mistrust
_____ 5. adolescence	E. identity vs. role confusion
_____ 6. young adulthood	F. industry vs. inferiority
_____ 7. middle adulthood	G. autonomy vs. shame/doubt
_____ 8. later adulthood	H. intimacy vs. isolation

© 2012 Cengage Learning. All Rights Reserved. May not be scanned, copied or duplicated, or posted to a publicly accessible website, in whole or in part.

Short Answer

Read each question. Think about the information presented in the text, and then answer each question.

1. Who developed the five stages of dying?

   _____

   _____

   _____

2. What are the five stages of dying?

   _____

   _____

   _____

3. Why can the five stages of dying apply to any form of loss?

   _____

   _____

   _____

4. Do the five stages of dying proceed in a specific sequence?

   _____

   _____

   _____

5. What is a life review?

   _____

   _____

   _____

6. In the stages of dying, what is the denial stage?

   _____

   _____

   _____

7. In the stages of dying, what is the anger stage?

   _____

   _____

   _____

© 2012 Cengage Learning. All Rights Reserved. May not be scanned, copied or duplicated, or posted to a publicly accessible website, in whole or in part.

8. In the stages of dying, what is the bargaining stage?

   _____

   _____

   _____

9. In the stages of dying, what is the depression stage?

   _____

   _____

   _____

10. In the stages of dying, what is the acceptance stage?

   _____

   _____

   _____

Critical Thinking Scenarios

Read each scenario. Think about the information presented in the text, and then answer each question.

1. Ms. Jennifer Chang brings her 5-year-old child to the clinic for a routine checkup.

   A. Which life stage would this child's age fall within?

   _____

   _____

   _____

   B. According to Erik Erikson's Stages of Psychosocial Development, what developmental stage does this age group address?

   _____

   _____

   _____

   C. What care considerations should be considered when working with this age group?

   _____

   _____

   _____

© 2012 Cengage Learning. All Rights Reserved. May not be scanned, copied or duplicated, or posted to a publicly accessible website, in whole or in part.

2. Whitney Comb is a retired financial planner. She is 80 years old and is at the provider's office due to concerns about increasing fatigue.

   A. Which life stage would this patient's age fall within?

   _____

   _____

   _____

   B. According to Erik Erikson's Stages of Psychosocial Development, what developmental stage does this age group address?

   _____

   _____

   _____

   C. What care considerations should be considered when working with this age group?

   _____

   _____

   _____

© 2012 Cengage Learning. All Rights Reserved. May not be scanned, copied or duplicated, or posted to a publicly accessible website, in whole or in part.

UNIT 4
Personal and Workplace Safety

© 2012 Cengage Learning. All Rights Reserved. May not be scanned, copied or duplicated, or posted to a publicly accessible website, in whole or in part.

CHAPTER 9

Body Mechanics

LEARNING OBJECTIVES

Studying and applying the material in this chapter will help you to:

- Understand and explain the importance of practicing good body mechanics and ergonomics at all times to prevent injury.
- Explain how repetitive injuries occur and how to prevent them.
- Demonstrate proper methods of sitting when working to prevent injury.
- Demonstrate proper methods of walking and standing at work to prevent injury.
- Demonstrate proper methods of lifting to prevent injury.
- Demonstrate proper methods of working at the computer to prevent injury.
- Properly use special adaptive devices to reduce the risk of workplace injuries.

VOCABULARY REVIEW

Definitions

Write the definition of each of the following words or terms.

1. body mechanics

   _____

   _____

   _____

2. ergonomics

   _____

   _____

   _____

© 2012 Cengage Learning. All Rights Reserved. May not be scanned, copied or duplicated, or posted to a publicly accessible website, in whole or in part.

3. repetitive motion injury (RMI)

_____

_____

_____

CHAPTER REVIEW

Identification 1

Place an "X" in front of the factors that can increase the likelihood of injury.

_____ 1. poor posture

_____ 2. poor body mechanics

_____ 3. low level of fitness

_____ 4. obesity

_____ 5. mechanical stress

_____ 6. psychological stress

Identification 2

Place an "X" in front of actions that specify proper sitting habits.

_____ 1. Do not use a chair back

_____ 2. Keep head and shoulders aligned over hips

_____ 3. When turning, pivot from the neck

_____ 4. Position chair so work is slightly below eye level

_____ 5. Place feet flat on the floor or on a footrest

Identification 3

Place an "X" in front of actions that specify proper standing or walking.

_____ 1. Keep neck in a neutral position

_____ 2. When standing, keep weight evenly distributed on both feet at all times

_____ 3. If possible, take off shoes and wear only socks or go barefoot

_____ 4. When standing, alternate placing one foot up on a footstool

_____ 5. Maintain the three normal curves of the back

© 2012 Cengage Learning. All Rights Reserved. May not be scanned, copied or duplicated, or posted to a publicly accessible website, in whole or in part.

Identification 4

Place an "X" in front of actions that specify proper lifting.

——— 1. Increase the base of support by positioning feet 12–15 inches apart

——— 2. Position your hands underneath the object to be lifted

——— 3. Exhale before lifting a heavy object

——— 4. Carry objects approximately 6 inches from the body at pelvic level

——— 5. When turning, move your entire body in unison

Identification 5

Place an "X" in front of recommendations to help prevent eyestrain.

——— 1. Keep the computer screen clean

——— 2. Rest the eyes every 1 to 2 hours

——— 3. Use glare screen on computer

——— 4. Use a paper holder to prevent having to look down to see text

——— 5. Adjust the contrast on the computer screen to a minimal level

True/False

Indicate whether the following statements are true (T) or false (F).

——— 1. Injuries are usually the result of poor practices over time that involve the repetition of improper movements.

——— 2. The greatest number of accidents in health care are the result of one-time incidents.

——— 3. Aging makes the health care professional more prone to injury.

——— 4. Most injuries are cumulative, and so it is habitual activity repeated over years that determines the future risk of injury.

——— 5. Ergonomics is the correct positioning of the body for a given task, such as lifting a heavy object or typing.

——— 6. Repetitive motion injuries (RMI) refer only to those injuries that are sustained while performing work duties.

——— 7. When standing in a static position, taking a break every two hours will avoid injury.

——— 8. Tension reduces blood circulation in the affected tissues and contributes to injury.

——— 9. Surgical intervention is the most common method of treating repetitive motion injuries (RMIs).

——— 10. Back injuries account for nearly 20% of all injuries and illnesses in the workplace.

——— 11. People who wear bifocals have an additional challenge to overcome when working on the computer.

© 2012 Cengage Learning. All Rights Reserved. May not be scanned, copied or duplicated, or posted to a publicly accessible website, in whole or in part.

Multiple Choice

Circle the best answer for each of the following questions. There is only one correct answer to each question.

1. Which of the following makes the health care professional more prone to injury?

   A. increased flexibility
   B. decreased flexibility
   C. decreased recovery time

2. Which of the following stressors contribute to work injuries?

   A. mechanical stress
   B. psychological stress
   C. both mechanical and psychological stresses

3. Which of the following is defined as using the correct positioning of the body for a given task?

   A. body mechanics
   B. ergonomics
   C. posture

4. Which systems are most often involved when a health care professional suffers a work injury?

   A. digestive and endocrine
   B. integumentary and sensory
   C. musculoskeletal and nervous

5. Which of the following repetitive motion injuries (RMIs) is caused by repeated hand motions that pinch a nerve in the wrist?

   A. carpal tunnel syndrome
   B. thoracic outlet syndrome
   C. tendonitis

6. Which of the following repetitive motion injuries (RMIs) is caused by repeated motions that compress nerves in the neck?

   A. carpal tunnel syndrome
   B. thoracic outlet syndrome
   C. tendonitis

7. Which of the following repetitive motion injuries (RMIs) is caused by repeated motion in a joint that inflames the tendons?

   A. carpal tunnel syndrome
   B. thoracic outlet syndrome
   C. tendonitis

8. Which of the following is a symptom of tendonitis?

   A. tenderness in the tendons of the shoulders, elbows, or hands
   B. tingling in the face and neck
   C. inability to make a fist

© 2012 Cengage Learning. All Rights Reserved. May not be scanned, copied or duplicated, or posted to a publicly accessible website, in whole or in part.

9. Which of the following is a symptom of thoracic outlet syndrome?

    A. inability to make a fist
    B. foot pain
    C. weakness in arms and hands

10. Which of the following is a symptom of carpal tunnel syndrome?

    A. leg pain
    B. loss of strength in the hand
    C. shoulder pain

11. Which of the following statements is true about the use of a mouse as a pointing device?

    A. It is effective in reducing injuries.
    B. It increases injuries.
    C. It has no impact on the injury rate.

Short Answer

Read each question. Think about the information presented in the text, and then answer each question.

1. What are the common symptoms of repetitive motion injuries (RMIs)?

    _____

    _____

    _____

2. List five conservative treatment measures for injuries.

    _____

    _____

    _____

3. What impact have computers had on the number of work injuries? List five preventive measures to follow while using a computer.

    _____

    _____

    _____

© 2012 Cengage Learning. All Rights Reserved. May not be scanned, copied or duplicated, or posted to a publicly accessible website, in whole or in part.

Critical Thinking Scenarios

Read each scenario. Think about the information presented in the text, and then answer each question.

1. Martha Zamboni is a 55-year-old health care professional. She is exhausted by her demanding schedule and family and social responsibilities. She keeps setting start dates to begin eating healthy and start exercising. She is 5′5″ tall and weighs 180 pounds.

   A. Is Martha at a higher risk for injury?

   _____

   _____

   _____

   B. What factors put her at risk?

   _____

   _____

   _____

   C. What preventive measures could she take to decrease her risk?

   _____

   _____

   _____

2. Peter Phillips is a health care professional whose job requires a lot of lifting and carrying of heavy items. He says he has heard some good things about back belts and asks your opinion.

   A. Should you recommend he wear a back belt?

   _____

   _____

   _____

   B. What are the possible advantages to wearing a back belt?

   _____

   _____

   _____

   C. What are the possible disadvantages to wearing a back belt?

   _____

   _____

   _____

© 2012 Cengage Learning. All Rights Reserved. May not be scanned, copied or duplicated, or posted to a publicly accessible website, in whole or in part.

CHAPTER 10

Infection Control

LEARNING OBJECTIVES

Studying and applying the material in this chapter will help you to:

- Understand and explain the importance of infection control practices in maintaining the safety of the health care professional, patients, and others.

- List the milestones that led to the development of germ theory and infection control.

- Identify the five types of microbes and give examples of infectious diseases caused by each type.

- Describe the chain of infection and list methods the health care professional can use to break it.

- Give examples of the body's defense mechanisms.

- Describe the CDC and OSHA and explain their roles in health care safety.

- Identify the preventive procedures included in the standard precautions.

- Identify situations when handwashing is indicated and demonstrate the technique.

- Identify the three types of transmission-based precautions and when they may be used.

- Describe neutropenic precautions and when they would be used.

- Explain the differences among antiseptics, disinfectants, and sterilization.

- Identify and describe the three major disease risks for health care professionals.

- Describe how pathogens become drug resistant and the impact this has on health care.

- Describe measures that will protect the health care professional and others from blood-borne pathogens.

© 2012 Cengage Learning. All Rights Reserved. May not be scanned, copied or duplicated, or posted to a publicly accessible website, in whole or in part.

VOCABULARY REVIEW

Definitions

Write the definition of each of the following words or terms.

1. aerobic

   _____

   _____

   _____

2. AIDS

   _____

   _____

   _____

3. anaerobic

   _____

   _____

   _____

4. antibiotic

   _____

   _____

   _____

5. antiseptics

   _____

   _____

   _____

6. asepsis or aseptic technique

   _____

   _____

   _____

7. bacteria

   _____

   _____

   _____

© 2012 Cengage Learning. All Rights Reserved. May not be scanned, copied or duplicated, or posted to a publicly accessible website, in whole or in part.

8. bacteriocidal

_____

_____

_____

9. bacteriostatic

_____

_____

_____

10. Centers for Disease Control and Prevention (CDC)

_____

_____

_____

11. chain of infection

_____

_____

_____

12. communicable disease

_____

_____

_____

13. contaminated

_____

_____

_____

14. disinfectants

_____

_____

_____

15. fungi (pl. of fungus)

_____

_____

_____

© 2012 Cengage Learning. All Rights Reserved. May not be scanned, copied or duplicated, or posted to a publicly accessible website, in whole or in part.

Matching 1

Match the following terms with their correct definitions.

_____ 1. germ theory

_____ 2. hepatitis B

_____ 3. HIV positive

_____ 4. host

_____ 5. immune response

_____ 6. infection control

_____ 7. infectious disease

_____ 8. medical asepsis or clean technique

_____ 9. microbes

_____ 10. microbiology

_____ 11. microorganisms

_____ 12. microscope

_____ 13. neutropenic precautions

_____ 14. normal flora

_____ 15. nosocomial infection

A. states that specific microorganisms called bacteria are the cause of specific diseases in both humans and animals

B. living plants or animals from which microorganisms derive nourishment

C. procedures to decrease the numbers and spread of pathogens in the environment

D. scientific study of microorganisms

E. isolation procedures to protect an immunocompromised patient from infections

F. infection that occurs while the patient is receiving health care

G. microorganisms that commonly reside in a particular environment on or in the body

H. instrument fitted with a powerful magnifying lens

I. small, usually one-celled living plants or animals

J. microorganisms that are pathogenic

K. disease caused by growth of pathogens

L. a virus that causes a blood-borne infection. An occupational hazard for health care workers

M. the condition of being infected by the human immunodeficiency virus

N. defense used by the body to fight infection and disease by producing antibodies

O. procedures to be followed to prevent the spread of infectious diseases

© 2012 Cengage Learning. All Rights Reserved. May not be scanned, copied or duplicated, or posted to a publicly accessible website, in whole or in part.

Word Fill

Complete the following sentences by filling in the missing words.

opportunistic infections	Occupational Safety and Health Administration	parasite	pathogens
		standard precautions	sterile field
protozoa	rickettsia	transmission-based precautions	tuberculosis (TB)
sterilization	surgical asepsis or sterile technique		
viruses			

1. The abbreviation OSHA stands for _____.

2. A/An _____ is an area designated to be free of microorganisms.

3. _____ are infections that occurs due to the weakened physiological state of the body.

4. _____ are the smallest of the microbes; they cannot be seen under normal light.

5. _____ uses agents or methods that totally destroy all microorganisms, including viruses and spores.

6. A/An _____ is an organism that nourishes itself at the expense of other living things and causes them damage.

7. _____ are procedures to completely eliminate the presence of pathogens from objects and areas.

8. _____ are practices designed to reduce the risk of transmission of microorganisms from both recognized and unrecognized sources of infection in health care settings.

9. A/An _____ are disease-causing microorganisms.

10. _____ include three types of isolation procedures (airborne, droplet, and contact precautions) required for specific infections.

11. _____ is a disease caused by the contagious, airborne pathogen *Mycobacterium tuberculosis*.

12. _____ are microorganisms that are classified as animals.

13. _____ are microorganisms that are smaller than bacteria and have rod or spherical shapes.

© 2012 Cengage Learning. All Rights Reserved. May not be scanned, copied or duplicated, or posted to a publicly accessible website, in whole or in part.

CHAPTER REVIEW

Identification 1

Place an "X" in front of the steps that are part of correct handwashing technique.

_____ 1. Keep hands lower than the elbow

_____ 2. Scrub palms in a circular motion while clasping hands together

_____ 3. Scrub wrists and forearms up to the elbows

_____ 4. Scrub hands for at least 2 minutes

_____ 5. Rinse thoroughly with warm running water from the wrists down to the fingertips

_____ 6. Clean under the nails with a cuticle stick, a brush, a fingernail, or by rubbing it against the palm of the other hand

_____ 7. Use bar soap and create a good lather

Identification 2

Place an "X" in front of the items that are considered personal protective equipment (PPE).

_____ 1. masks

_____ 2. glasses/goggles

_____ 3. gowns

_____ 4. caps

_____ 5. dressings

_____ 6. gloves

True/False

Indicate whether the following statements are true (T) or false (F).

_____ 1. Medical asepsis is also known as sterile technique.

_____ 2. The Centers of Disease Control and Prevention (CDC) and the Occupational Safety and Health Administration (OSHA) are both governmental agencies.

_____ 3. Someone with a nosocomial infection should be placed in isolation.

_____ 4. Flagella are whip-like appendages that help certain bacteria move.

_____ 5. Viruses are obligate intracellular organisms.

_____ 6. Normal flora is a common source of infection.

_____ 7. Escherichia coli (E. coli) can be both pathogenic and nonpathogenic.

© 2012 Cengage Learning. All Rights Reserved. May not be scanned, copied or duplicated, or posted to a publicly accessible website, in whole or in part.

_____ 8. An immune response is an abnormal response of the body.

_____ 9. Generalized infections can easily be treated by applying a local antibiotic.

_____ 10. An anaerobic microorganism does not require oxygen to live.

Matching 2

Match the following terms with their correct definitions.

_____ 1. bacteria

A. Used with infectious organisms that can be propelled short distance through the air

_____ 2. viruses

B. Only microbes that are classified as animals

_____ 3. fungi

C. Used when infectious organisms are transmitted by touching of skin or other surfaces

_____ 4. rickettsia

D. Used for patients very susceptible to infections

_____ 5. protozoa

E. Smaller than bacteria and have rod or spherical shapes

_____ 6. airborne precautions

F. Smallest of the microbes

_____ 7. droplet precautions

G. One-celled plants

_____ 8. contact precautions

H. Used for patients with diagnosis of Mucobacterium tuberculosis

_____ 9. standard precautions

I. Large group of simple plants

_____ 10. neutropenic precautions

J. Must be used at all times to prevent contact with potentially infectious body fluids

Matching 3

Match the following terms with their correct definitions.

_____ 1. avian influenza

A. Transmitted by infected mosquitoes to humans and animals

_____ 2. bovine spongiform encephalopathy

B. Caused by a resistant strain of staphylococcus aureus

_____ 3. West Nile virus

C. Transmitted by infected birds

_____ 4. H1N1 influenza

D. Caused by a resistant strain of enterococci

_____ 5. MRSA

E. Spread mainly person-to-person

_____ 6. VRE

F. Thought to be caused by a type of protein, called prions, normally found in animals

© 2012 Cengage Learning. All Rights Reserved. May not be scanned, copied or duplicated, or posted to a publicly accessible website, in whole or in part.

Short Answer

Read each question. Think about the information presented in the text, and then answer each question.

1. List three of the natural defense mechanisms of the body.

   _____

   _____

   _____

2. What is the difference between medical asepsis and surgical asepsis?

   _____

   _____

   _____

3. How can the health care professional decrease the source of microorganisms?

   _____

   _____

   _____

4. How can the health care professional prevent the transmission of microorganisms?

   _____

   _____

   _____

5. How can the health care professional maximize the resistance of the host?

   _____

   _____

   _____

6. List the various hepatitis viruses and how they are transmitted.

   _____

   _____

   _____

7. What is the difference between HIV positive and AIDS?

   _____

   _____

   _____

8. Explain how someone can have a positive TB skin test and not have active tuberculosis.

   _____

   _____

   _____

© 2012 Cengage Learning. All Rights Reserved. May not be scanned, copied or duplicated, or posted to a publicly accessible website, in whole or in part.

9. What are the signs and symptoms of active TB disease?

_____

_____

_____

10. Why is it important to immediately report accidental exposures to blood or body fluids to the supervisor?

_____

_____

_____

Labeling

Assign the labels from the list to the appropriate places on the figure.

Figure 10-1 Chain of Infection

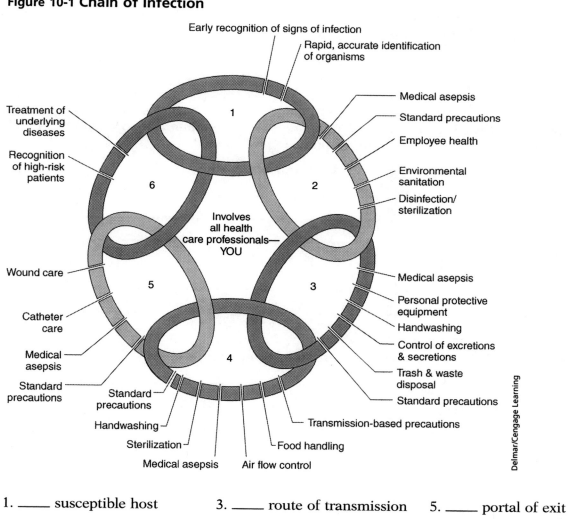

1. _____ susceptible host   3. _____ route of transmission   5. _____ portal of exit

2. _____ infectious agent   4. _____ portal of entry   6. _____ reservoir host

© 2012 Cengage Learning. All Rights Reserved. May not be scanned, copied or duplicated, or posted to a publicly accessible website, in whole or in part.

Critical Thinking Scenarios

Read each scenario. Think about the information presented in the text, and then answer each question.

1. Magreet Hawking is very concerned about getting swine flu and has many questions when she comes to the health care facility.

    A. How is H1N1 transmitted?

    _____

    _____

    _____

    B. What are the common symptoms?

    _____

    _____

    _____

    C. What preventive measures can she use?

    _____

    _____

    _____

2. Stephen Quest has been reading about the increase in community-associated MRSA and asks for more information from his health care professional.

    A. What is the difference between HA-MRSA and CA-MRSA?

    _____

    _____

    _____

    B. What has caused the development of resistant bacteria?

    _____

    _____

    _____

    C. What can he do to decrease the chances of contracting a CA-MRSA infection?

    _____

    _____

    _____

© 2012 Cengage Learning. All Rights Reserved. May not be scanned, copied or duplicated, or posted to a publicly accessible website, in whole or in part.

D. How can you as a health care professional help prevent your patients from developing a HA-MRSA?

_____

_____

_____

Procedure Assessments

Complete the procedure assessments for this chapter at the end of the workbook.

© 2012 Cengage Learning. All Rights Reserved. May not be scanned, copied or duplicated, or posted to a publicly accessible website, in whole or in part.

CHAPTER 11

Environmental Safety

LEARNING OBJECTIVES

Studying and applying the material in this chapter will help you to:

- Understand and explain the importance of environmental safety in maintaining the safety of the health care professional, the patients, and others.

- Identify general safety guidelines that will help prevent injuries and accidents in health care facilities.

- Describe and give examples of how changes in the physical and mental health of a patient can increase the risk of injuries and accidents.

- Define what workplace violence is and discuss preventive measures.

- Describe and explain the purpose of an incident report.

- Identify the appropriate steps to take in the event of a fire.

- Identify the different classes of fire extinguishers and type of fire on which to use each.

- List ways to prevent electrical hazards.

- Discuss chemical, radiation, and infectious hazards and the role of the health care professional in their prevention.

- Describe the precautions necessary when oxygen is in use.

- Explain when an emergency disaster plan would be implemented and define a triage system.

© 2012 Cengage Learning. All Rights Reserved. May not be scanned, copied or duplicated, or posted to a publicly accessible website, in whole or in part.

VOCABULARY

Definitions

Write the definition of each of the following words or terms.

1. compatibility

   _____

   _____

   _____

2. flammable

   _____

   _____

   _____

3. toxic

   _____

   _____

   _____

Matching 1

Match the following terms with their correct definitions.

_____ 1. emergency disaster plan

_____ 2. environmental safety

_____ 3. incident report

_____ 4. inflammable

_____ 5. PASS

_____ 6. RACE

_____ 7. triage system

A. guidelines to determine which patients to send where and what treatment will be given during an emergency

B. written document that is filled out when any unexpected situation occurs that can cause harm to a patient, employee, or any other person

C. policy and procedures to be followed when an event occurs that has the potential to kill or injure a group of people

D. acronym for responding to fires

E. acronym for proper use of a portable fire extinguisher

F. easily set on fire; same as flammable

G. the identification and correction of potential hazards that can cause accidents and injuries

© 2012 Cengage Learning. All Rights Reserved. May not be scanned, copied or duplicated, or posted to a publicly accessible website, in whole or in part.

CHAPTER REVIEW

True/False

Indicate whether the following statements are true (T) or false (F).

_____ 1. Patients have the right to refuse any procedure or medication.

_____ 2. You can leave a patient unattended on a treatment table if they are alert and oriented.

_____ 3. If a patient is hard of hearing the best approach is to yell very loudly when communicating.

_____ 4. If the patient has tremors or shaking it may be a sign of an altered neurological function.

_____ 5. Patients taking medications should be observed for changes that can affect their safety.

_____ 6. The health care area is a very safe place to work, and health care professionals are rarely exposed to safety and health hazards.

_____ 7. Fires in health care facilities can result from a number of hazards.

_____ 8. It is critical to stay calm during an emergency.

_____ 9. A policy that many facilities have is that no personal electrical equipment can be brought into the hospital because the possibility of it being defective is a fire risk.

_____ 10. When smoke is present during a fire it is best to walk upright as there will be more oxygen at higher levels.

Multiple Choice

Circle the best answer for each of the following questions. There is only one correct answer to each question.

1. When would it be appropriate to run in a health care facility?

   A. in an emergency
   B. during a fire
   C. never

2. Which side of the hallway should be walked on in a health care facility?

   A. right
   B. left
   C. center

© 2012 Cengage Learning. All Rights Reserved. May not be scanned, copied or duplicated, or posted to a publicly accessible website, in whole or in part.

3. When is it appropriate to wear earrings in a health care facility?

   A. never
   B. when they do not extend beyond the earlobe
   C. when you are not working with combative patients

4. What is the main reason for keeping fingernails short when working in a health care facility?

   A. prevents scratching of patients
   B. prevents painful tears when they catch on items
   C. they harbor bacteria

5. What type of jewelry is acceptable in the health care facility?

   A. smooth wedding band
   B. necklaces but not rings or bracelets
   C. no jewelry should be worn

6. How should hair be worn when working in a health care facility?

   A. any style as long as it is kept out of your eyes
   B. tie long hair back or up
   C. place long hair under your collar when bending over patients

7. What type of shoes are to be worn in the health care environment?

   A. only those that have very cushioned soles
   B. any type as long as they are comfortable
   C. enclosed shoes

8. Which of the following ways of identifying patients would be the best?

   A. have them state their name
   B. ask them "Are you ...?"
   C. have them state their full name and birthdate

9. In what locations is it appropriate to wear your uniform?

   A. only in the work setting
   B. when running an errand right after work
   C. anytime as long as it is clean

10. When should unsafe conditions be reported?

    A. immediately
    B. before the end of your shift
    C. only if you are sure no one else has already made a report

© 2012 Cengage Learning. All Rights Reserved. May not be scanned, copied or duplicated, or posted to a publicly accessible website, in whole or in part.

Matching 2

Match the following types of hazards with their descriptions.

—— 1. chemical

—— 2. environmental

—— 3. ergonomic

—— 4. infectious

—— 5. physical

—— 6. psychosocial

—— 7. workplace violence

A. agents that can cause physical injury and tissue damage

B. unsafe conditions in the workplace

C. stressors causing anxiety and emotional fatigue

D. substances with toxic effects when inhaled, ingested, or with skin contact

E. microbes that can cause infections

F. unsafe workplace design

G. physical or verbal abuse

Short Answer

Read each question. Think about the information presented in the text, and then answer each question.

1. List the various types of fire and which fire extinguishers should be used for each type.

_____

_____

_____

2. Explain what the acronym RACE stands for.

_____

_____

_____

3. Explain what the acronym PASS stands for.

_____

_____

_____

© 2012 Cengage Learning. All Rights Reserved. May not be scanned, copied or duplicated, or posted to a publicly accessible website, in whole or in part.

4. What are radiation hazards and how are employees protected?

_____

_____

_____

5. Why are special precautions needed when a patient is receiving oxygen therapy?

_____

_____

_____

6. What is an emergency disaster plan?

_____

_____

_____

7. What is a triage system?

_____

_____

_____

Ordering

Place the following duties in the order in which they should be performed when using a fire extinguisher. Put a numeral 1 before the first duty, a 2 before the next, and so on.

_____ 1. sweep back and forth along the base of the fire

_____ 2. pull the pin

_____ 3. aim the nozzle at the base of the fire

_____ 4. squeeze the handle

© 2012 Cengage Learning. All Rights Reserved. May not be scanned, copied or duplicated, or posted to a publicly accessible website, in whole or in part.

Labeling

Assign the labels in the list to the appropriate places on the figure.

Figure 11-1

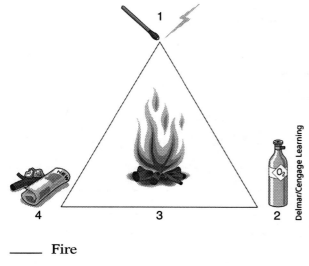

_____ Fire

_____ Heat

_____ Oxygen

_____ Fuel

Assign the labels in the list to the appropriate places on the figure.

Figure 11-2

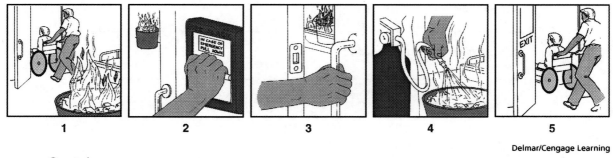

Delmar/Cengage Learning

_____ Contain

_____ Remove

_____ Evacuate

_____ Extinguish or

_____ Activate alarm

© 2012 Cengage Learning. All Rights Reserved. May not be scanned, copied or duplicated, or posted to a publicly accessible website, in whole or in part.

Critical Thinking Scenarios

Read each scenario. Think about the information presented in the text, and then answer each question.

1. Mr. Amos Scruthers is concerned about recent articles he has read on bioterrorism and starts to express concern to you while at the health care facility.

   A. Is bioterrorism a new occurrence specific to our current times?

   _____

   _____

   _____

   B. Do health care facilities have any plans in the event of a bioterrorism attack?

   _____

   _____

   _____

   C. What are the most likely threat agents and what precautions would be used?

   _____

   _____

   _____

2. Randy Johnson just accepted a position at the emergency room of a local hospital. He has heard that emergency rooms tend to have more workplace violence and is nervous.

   A. What actions constitute workplace violence?

   _____

   _____

   _____

   B. How common is workplace violence?

   _____

   _____

   _____

   C. What is the source of the most common workplace violence?

   _____

   _____

   _____

   D. What can he do to protect himself?

   _____

   _____

   _____

© 2012 Cengage Learning. All Rights Reserved. May not be scanned, copied or duplicated, or posted to a publicly accessible website, in whole or in part.

UNIT 5
Behaviors for Success

© 2012 Cengage Learning. All Rights Reserved. May not be scanned, copied or duplicated, or posted to a publicly accessible website, in whole or in part.

CHAPTER 12

Lifestyle Management

LEARNING OBJECTIVES

Studying and applying the material in this chapter will help you to:

■ Explain the importance of developing a healthy lifestyle.

■ State the principles of habit formation.

■ List the essential nutrients and the function of each.

■ Describe how each of the following contributes to healthy living: diet, physical activity, sleep, and preventive measures.

■ Define stress and list several common causes.

■ Describe five ways of effectively dealing with stress.

■ Explain the major health risks encountered by the health care professional.

■ List the causes and symptoms of and preventive measures for burnout.

■ Explain how health care professionals can help patients develop good health habits.

VOCABULARY REVIEW

Definitions

Write the definition of each of the following words or terms.

1. assertiveness

_____

_____

_____

2. attitude

_____

_____

_____

© 2012 Cengage Learning. All Rights Reserved. May not be scanned, copied or duplicated, or posted to a publicly accessible website, in whole or in part.

3. meditation

_____

_____

_____

4. prioritize

_____

_____

_____

5. relaxation (muscles)

_____

_____

_____

6. stress

_____

_____

_____

7. stressor

_____

_____

_____

Matching 1

Match the following terms with their correct definitions.

_____ 1. amino acids   A. food substances that provide the most concentrated form of energy

_____ 2. carbohydrates   B. the basic components of protein

_____ 3. fats   C. inorganic substances needed for certain body functions

_____ 4. fiber   D. food substances needed for building and maintaining body structures

_____ 5. minerals   E. food products that cannot be digested

_____ 6. proteins   F. organic substances needed to maintain health

_____ 7. vitamins   G. food substances made up of sugar that provide the body with quick energy

© 2012 Cengage Learning. All Rights Reserved. May not be scanned, copied or duplicated, or posted to a publicly accessible website, in whole or in part.

Matching 2

Match the following terms with their correct definitions.

_____ 1. cholesterol

_____ 2. diet

_____ 3. free radicals

_____ 4. legumes

_____ 5. nutrients

_____ 6. nutrition

_____ 7. trans fat

A. molecules with unpaired electrons that can damage the body's cells

B. a class of plants that includes peas, beans, peanuts, lentils, and soybeans

C. the process of obtaining food necessary for health and growth

D. the foods a person customarily eats

E. fatty substances, contained in certain foods, that can accumulate in the arteries

F. substances the body needs to function and grow

G. vegetable oil that contains added hydrogen and has the capacity to raise "bad cholesterol" levels in the blood

Word Fill 1

Complete the following sentences by filling in the missing words.

metabolism	calories	aerobic	Food Guide Pyramid
organic	body mass index		

1. _____ exercise increases the strength of the heart muscle.

2. The measurement of the relationship of weight to height using a mathematical formula is called the _____.

3. _____ are units of energy from food that the body uses to function or store as fat.

4. The U.S. Department of Agriculture developed the _____ to help individuals plan meals that contain required nutrients.

5. The chemical process of converting nutrients into tissue and/or producing energy is called _____.

6. When referring to agricultural products, _____ describes certain production methods that include using natural rather than chemical fertilizers and pesticides.

© 2012 Cengage Learning. All Rights Reserved. May not be scanned, copied or duplicated, or posted to a publicly accessible website, in whole or in part.

Word Fill 2

Complete the following sentences by filling in the missing words.

overweight   bulimia   obese   type 2 diabetes

anorexia nervosa   burnout   osteoporosis   binge eating

1. _____ is a serious physical and psychological disorder characterized by refusing to eat enough to maintain good health.

2. An individual who engages in _____ compulsively eats large amounts of food, beyond what is needed to satisfy physical hunger.

3. Individuals who make themselves vomit after eating in order to avoid weight gain may be suffering from _____.

4. Feeling exhausted and unappreciated, along with losing interest in one's job, are signs of _____.

5. Harold's physician told him he is now _____, having reaching a BMI of 32.

6. Many older adults have _____, a condition characterized by bones that have lost their density and are easily fractured.

7. At least 67% of Americans are now either _____ or obese.

8. _____ is a serious chronic disease in which blood sugar levels are abnormally high.

CHAPTER REVIEW

True/False

Indicate whether the following statements are true (T) or false (F).

_____ 1. Many serious health conditions, such as heart disease, are strongly influenced by lifestyle habits.

_____ 2. Most people with arthritis feel better if they avoid physical exercise.

_____ 3. Physical exercise promotes the body's production of endorphins.

_____ 4. Most people do best when they get about six hours of sleep each night.

_____ 5. It is recommended that adults get at least one hour of physical activity every day.

_____ 6. People who have trouble sleeping may find that avoiding stressful activities in the evening improves their sleep.

_____ 7. Gum disease is usually not serious and can be ignored as long as it isn't painful.

_____ 8. Health care professionals who may contact body fluids should be immunized against hepatitis B.

_____ 9. Stress is defined as an emotional reaction to an irritating or annoying event.

© 2012 Cengage Learning. All Rights Reserved. May not be scanned, copied or duplicated, or posted to a publicly accessible website, in whole or in part.

—— 10. A good way to maintain good health is to avoid all stressful situations.

—— 11. When faced with many responsibilities, it is best to do the easiest tasks first.

—— 12. Meditating regularly can bring about positive physiological changes.

True/False Rewrite

Please rewrite the bold part of the sentence to make the statement true.

1. Fiber is needed only by **persons who have digestive problems**.

   _____

   _____

   _____

2. Developing healthy habits **is easy** for individuals with strong willpower and self-discipline.

   _____

   _____

   _____

3. A healthy diet should contain adequate amounts of protein and **no fats**.

   _____

   _____

   _____

4. Foods containing high amounts of **proteins**, such as fish, provide the most concentrated forms of energy.

   _____

   _____

   _____

5. Water makes up about **40 percent** of the average person's total body weight.

   _____

   _____

   _____

6. Amino acids are important components of **carbohydrates**.

   _____

   _____

   _____

7. A diet to help prevent osteoporosis should include high amounts of **vitamin C**.

   _____

   _____

   _____

© 2012 Cengage Learning. All Rights Reserved. May not be scanned, copied or duplicated, or posted to a publicly accessible website, in whole or in part.

8. A gram of fat contains **five calories**.

_____

_____

_____

9. **Eggs and cheese** are good sources of omega-3 fatty acids.

_____

_____

_____

10. Approximately **40 percent** of the adults in the United States are either overweight or obese.

_____

_____

_____

Matching 3

Match the following vitamins with their functions. (Note: two of the vitamins perform the same function.)

_____ 1. vitamin A

_____ 2. thiamin

_____ 3. riboflavin

_____ 4. niacin

_____ 5. vitamin B_6

_____ 6. vitamin B_{12}

_____ 7. vitamin C

_____ 8. vitamin D

_____ 9. vitamin E

_____ 10. vitamin K

A. production of energy from carbohydrates

B. manufacture of amino acids and red blood cells

C. normal function of muscles

D. healing of wounds; healthy bones and gums

E. growth; prevention of infection

F. absorption of calcium

G. metabolism of nutrients into energy

H. clotting of blood

I. production of red blood cells; maintenance of nervous system

© 2012 Cengage Learning. All Rights Reserved. May not be scanned, copied or duplicated, or posted to a publicly accessible website, in whole or in part.

Matching 4

Match the following minerals with their functions.

____ 1. calcium

____ 2. folate

____ 3. iron

____ 4. magnesium

____ 5. phosphorus

____ 6. potassium

____ 7. zinc

A. nerve function; muscle contraction

B. transport of oxygen in red blood cells

C. growth and repair of supportive tissue

D. DNA synthesis in making protein

E. energy production; nerve function

F. reproduction of cells; tissue growth and repair

G. building and maintenance of bones

Short Answer

Read each question. Think about the information presented in the text, and then answer each question.

1. List four factors that contribute to the growing problem of substance abuse among health care professionals.

_____

_____

_____

2. Approximately how many deaths each year have smoking as a contributing cause?

_____

_____

_____

3. What is the difference between internal and external stressors?

_____

_____

_____

4. How does relaxing the muscles help relieve feelings of anxiety?

_____

_____

_____

© 2012 Cengage Learning. All Rights Reserved. May not be scanned, copied or duplicated, or posted to a publicly accessible website, in whole or in part.

5. What are five positive effects when meditation is practiced over an extended period of time?

_____

_____

_____

6. What are four ways that individuals can protect themselves against sexually transmitted diseases?

_____

_____

_____

7. List six occupational stressors that can lead to burnout.

_____

_____

_____

8. List at least six conditions and diseases related to overweight and obesity.

_____

_____

_____

9. List five methods that have been found helpful for individuals who want to quit smoking.

_____

_____

_____

10. What is the formula for calculating body mass index?

_____

_____

_____

© 2012 Cengage Learning. All Rights Reserved. May not be scanned, copied or duplicated, or posted to a publicly accessible website, in whole or in part.

Completion

Use the words in the list to complete the following statements:

high quality	nutrients	reasonable	responsibility
addictive substances	energy	role models	sleep
progress	arthritis		

1. Some habits, such as smoking, are difficult to change because they involve _____.

2. When working to achieve goals, it can be helpful to track your _____ on a chart.

3. Good health is about more than living a long time; it is also about living a _____ life.

4. Medical science can help solve many problems, but individuals must take _____ for their own health.

5. Today's health care professionals should serve as _____ for their patients and for society as a whole.

6. When working to change lifestyle habits, it is best to set _____ goals.

7. Muscle tissue uses more _____ to support itself than does fat tissue.

8. When choosing an eating plan to lose weight, it is important to make sure that all essential _____ are included.

9. One of the many benefits of physical exercise is that it can decrease the pain of _____.

10. Body temperature decreases and functions slow down during _____.

Critical Thinking Scenarios

Read each scenario. Think about the information presented in the text, and then answer each question.

1. Janna is a practical nurse. She has been working at a nursing home for the last three years. There has been a lot of turnover among staff and she is frequently asked to work extra hours. Many of the residents are elderly and die within months of being admitted. Janna is becoming increasingly unhappy with her job.

   A. What is the name of the condition that Janna may be experiencing?

   _____

   _____

   _____

B. What are signs of this condition?

_____

_____

_____

C. What can Janna do to counteract this condition?

_____

_____

_____

2. Earl has a part-time job in addition to his respiratory therapy classes. After studying in the evenings, he finds he is "wound up" and likes to relax by watching television until rather late. Recently, he has found it difficult to concentrate during lectures and when doing his reading assignments.

A. Explain how Earl's late nights may be contributing to his difficulty concentrating.

_____

_____

_____

B. When does mental recuperation take place during sleep?

_____

_____

_____

C. What are some methods Earl might use to increase the quality and quantity of sleep?

_____

_____

_____

© 2012 Cengage Learning. All Rights Reserved. May not be scanned, copied or duplicated, or posted to a publicly accessible website, in whole or in part.

CHAPTER 13

Professionalism

LEARNING OBJECTIVES

Studying and applying the material in this chapter will help you to:

- Explain the meaning of professionalism for individuals who work in health care.
- Describe each of the following components of professionalism:
  - Attitude
  - Behaviors
  - Health care skills
  - Appearance
- Explain the meaning of "professional distance."
- Explain how health care professionals can effectively handle difficult situations.
- Describe how to accept criticism professionally.
- Explain how professional organizations help individuals who work in health care increase their level of professionalism.
- Identify the characteristics of a health care leader.

VOCABULARY REVIEW

Definitions

Write the definition of each of the following words or terms.

1. continuing education

   _____

   _____

   _____

© 2012 Cengage Learning. All Rights Reserved. May not be scanned, copied or duplicated, or posted to a publicly accessible website, in whole or in part.

2. leadership

_____

_____

_____

3. objective (adjective)

_____

_____

_____

4. professional distance

_____

_____

_____

5. professionalism

_____

_____

_____

CHAPTER REVIEW

True/False

Indicate whether the following statements are true (T) or false (F).

_____ 1. Pain and fear can cause patients to behave rudely.

_____ 2. It is inappropriate for a supervisor to ask an employee to do extra work that is not part of the employee's job description.

_____ 3. It is a good idea to get your coworkers' opinions about how to handle problems you are having with your supervisor.

_____ 4. Even experienced health care professionals need to pay attention and think about what they are doing at work.

_____ 5. It is appropriate to ask your supervisor about a situation that does not seem right given the circumstances.

_____ 6. The appearance of health professionals is not important as long as they are competent.

_____ 7. Health care professionals should not seek the friendship and approval of their patients.

_____ 8. Understanding the theories that support your skills is not important if you can perform the skills accurately and safely.

© 2012 Cengage Learning. All Rights Reserved. May not be scanned, copied or duplicated, or posted to a publicly accessible website, in whole or in part.

——— 9. Most health care professional organizations take care not to get involved with politics at any level.

——— 10. Good leaders do not necessarily have supervisory positions.

Multiple Choice

Circle the best answer for each of the following questions. There is only one correct answer to each question.

1. Maintaining professional distance means _____.
   A. not invading a patient's personal space
   B. not becoming emotionally involved with patients
   C. taking care not to spread infections from one patient to another

2. Kim often has her feelings hurt when patients are not appreciative of her efforts to help them. She should _____.
   A. ask her supervisor for help with this problem
   B. let her patients know they have hurt her feelings
   C. explore why she feels the need for approval

3. When encountering a difficult situation on the job, it is recommended that health care professionals _____.
   A. ignore the situation and continue with their work
   B. apply the five-step problem-solving process
   C. ask their supervisor to take care of the problem

4. Larry's supervisor criticized his technique in delivering a breathing treatment. The best course of action for Larry is to _____.
   A. ask his supervisor for help in perfecting his technique
   B. tell his supervisor that this is how he learned the technique in school
   C. ignore the criticism

5. When patients complain to Gayle, a dietetic technician, about the diets their doctors have prescribed, she should _____.
   A. say that she is just following the doctor's orders
   B. tell them it's okay for them to "cheat" a little
   C. explain how the diet will improve their health

6. Which of the following best demonstrates the meaning of leadership?
   A. receiving a promotion at work
   B. inspiring coworkers to meet team goals
   C. volunteering to work extra hours

7. Being committed to your work is best demonstrated by _____.
   A. always putting the needs of patients before your own
   B. believing in the value of your work with patients
   C. developing emotional attachments with your patients

© 2012 Cengage Learning. All Rights Reserved. May not be scanned, copied or duplicated, or posted to a publicly accessible website, in whole or in part.

8. The most effective approach to problems in the workplace is _____.

    A. objective
    B. subjective
    C. biased

9. Tishia, a dental hygienist, is experiencing serious personal problems. It would be best for her to _____.

    A. let off steam by discussing her problems with coworkers
    B. share them with her favorite patients
    C. keep them to herself while she is at work

10. If you are unsure about a policy at your workplace, it is best to first _____.

    A. check the employee manual
    B. ask your supervisor
    C. ask a coworker

Short Answer

Read each question. Think about the information presented in the text, and then answer each question.

1. List eight behaviors that are expressions of professional conduct.

    _____

    _____

    _____

2. What are five characteristics of a professional attitude?

    _____

    _____

    _____

3. What are five characteristics of professional hygiene and appearance?

    _____

    _____

    _____

© 2012 Cengage Learning. All Rights Reserved. May not be scanned, copied or duplicated, or posted to a publicly accessible website, in whole or in part.

4. What benefits do health care professionals receive when they are active in their professional organizations?

_____

_____

_____

5. Why is it important for the health care professional to be well organized?

_____

_____

_____

6. What are possible consequences of health care professionals complaining to coworkers and patients about their jobs?

_____

_____

_____

7. How can problems in the workplace be viewed as opportunities?

_____

_____

_____

8. Why is it important to understand the theories that support your technical skills?

_____

_____

_____

© 2012 Cengage Learning. All Rights Reserved. May not be scanned, copied or duplicated, or posted to a publicly accessible website, in whole or in part.

9. Explain the possible effects of a health care professional's appearance and hygiene on patients.

_____

_____

_____

10. Why is it important for health care professionals to remain calm in emergency situations?

_____

_____

_____

Completion

Use the words in the list to complete the following statements:

self-discipline	flexible	malpractice lawsuits	patient welfare
personal problems	caring competence	objective	dependability
patient satisfaction	attitude		

1. _____ is an effective way to describe professionalism in health care.

2. Approaching work positively is a sign of a good _____.

3. The primary focus of a good health care professional is _____.

4. Taking a/an _____ approach to a situation means basing decisions on facts rather than emotions and opinions.

5. The conduct of individual health care professionals influences _____ with the facility in which the professionals work.

6. When patients feel they have received poor service, even if treatment outcomes are positive, they are more likely to file _____.

7. Knowing you can depend on yourself to complete your tasks is a sign of _____.

8. Health care professionals who follow through and complete their tasks are demonstrating _____.

9. It is necessary for health care professionals to be _____ because health care is constantly changing.

10. Health care professionals should never discuss _____ with their patients.

© 2012 Cengage Learning. All Rights Reserved. May not be scanned, copied or duplicated, or posted to a publicly accessible website, in whole or in part.

Critical Thinking Scenarios

Read each scenario. Think about the information presented in the text, and then answer each question.

1. Cindy is starting her first job since graduating as a veterinary technician. She studied hard throughout her program, but realizes that there are additional skills she needs to learn and master.

    A. Why is it important for Cindy to continue to work on her technical skills after graduation?

    _____

    _____

    _____

    B. What are ways she can further develop her skills?

    _____

    _____

    _____

2. Brad enjoys his work as a paramedic but was told by his supervisor that he needs to be "more professional" when on the job.

    A. How should Brad respond to his supervisor's comment?

    _____

    _____

    _____

    B. How should health care professionals behave when responding to emergencies?

    _____

    _____

    _____

© 2012 Cengage Learning. All Rights Reserved. May not be scanned, copied or duplicated, or posted to a publicly accessible website, in whole or in part.

CHAPTER 14

Lifelong Learning

LEARNING OBJECTIVES

Studying and applying the material in this chapter will help you to:

- Understand and explain the importance of lifelong learning for the health care professional.
- List the reasons for participating in continuing education opportunities.
- Describe ways you can earn continuing education credits.
- Create a personal plan for self-directed learning.

VOCABULARY REVIEW

Definitions

Write the definition of each of the following words or terms.

1. continuing education units

   _____

   _____

   _____

2. continuing professional education

   _____

   _____

   _____

3. demographics

   _____

   _____

   _____

© 2012 Cengage Learning. All Rights Reserved. May not be scanned, copied or duplicated, or posted to a publicly accessible website, in whole or in part.

4. lifelong learning

_____

_____

_____

5. self-directed learning

_____

_____

_____

CHAPTER REVIEW

True/False

Indicate whether the following statements are true (T) or false (F).

_____ 1. Technology is changing faster today than at any time in history.

_____ 2. Health care graduates will be required to continue learning throughout their careers.

_____ 3. Changes in health care have resulted in many professionals performing a more limited set of tasks.

_____ 4. Most certifying bodies require the completion of certain numbers of continuing education credits to renew certification.

_____ 5. One unit of continuing education credit typically requires 30 minutes of class attendance.

_____ 6. The school from which you graduated determines the number of continuing education units you will need to maintain your professional certification.

_____ 7. Most certifying bodies require that proof of professional education be retained for at least ten years.

_____ 8. There are currently more than 8,000 publications indexed by the National Library of Medicine.

_____ 9. Not all continuing education courses are accepted by the organizations that require the units for certification.

_____ 10. Online courses are not generally accepted for continuing education credit.

© 2012 Cengage Learning. All Rights Reserved. May not be scanned, copied or duplicated, or posted to a publicly accessible website, in whole or in part.

Matching

Match the following changes with corresponding learning activities for health care professionals.

_____ 1. people are living longer

                  A. acquire skills beyond those specific to one's profession

_____ 2. hospital stays are shorter

                  B. read about treatments such as acupuncture and meditation

_____ 3. increased ethnic diversity among patients

                  C. observe the use of new imaging machines

_____ 4. growing interest in complementary medicine

                  D. learn to use new software programs

_____ 5. more third-party payers

                  E. study the needs of older adults

_____ 6. emphasis on wellness and patient responsibility

                  F. learn about insurance requirements

_____ 7. heavy use of computers

                  G. develop communication skills that link team members

_____ 8. spread of HIV and other viruses

                  H. learn about the cultural groups that make up your patient population

_____ 9. expanded roles for health care professionals

                  I. learn and practice standard precautions

_____ 10. increased medical specialization

                  J. participate in vendor demonstrations of new equipment

_____ 11. increasingly sophisticated equipment

                  K. learn about healthy lifestyle practices

_____ 12. new diagnostic procedures and treatments

                  L. develop skill at delivering patient education on self-care practices

Short Answer

Read each question. Think about the information presented in the text, and then answer each question.

1. List five ways to earn continuing education units.

_____

_____

_____

2. What are five criteria for choosing useful, good quality continuing education?

_____

_____

_____

© 2012 Cengage Learning. All Rights Reserved. May not be scanned, copied or duplicated, or posted to a publicly accessible website, in whole or in part.

3. Describe four self-directed learning activities in which a health care professional might engage.

   _____

   _____

   _____

4. List six reliable health information websites.

   _____

   _____

   _____

5. Which segment of the population will make up most of the patient load in the next few years?

   _____

   _____

   _____

Completion

Use the words in the list to complete the following statements:

continuing education units	lifelong learning	certifying body	continuing professional education
traditional duties	demographics	Mondale Lifelong Learning Act of 1976	self-directed learning
certification	formal training		

1. _____ refers to what we do throughout our lives to acquire new information and skills.

2. The federal government recognized the need for adults to continue learning when it passed the _____.

3. Graduation marks the end of _____ and the beginning of lifelong learning.

4. Studies that monitor shifts in population and record statistics are known as _____.

5. Most health care professionals are required to earn _____ in order to keep their certifications current.

6. _____ is term for the education that follows graduation and keeps a health professional up-to-date in his or her field.

7. _____ refers to activities that you plan to acquire new information and skills on your own.

8. Providing documentation of learning beyond one's formal training is necessary to retain one's professional _____.

© 2012 Cengage Learning. All Rights Reserved. May not be scanned, copied or duplicated, or posted to a publicly accessible website, in whole or in part.

9. Many health care professionals are being required to expand their _____.

10. Be sure that any educational activity you engage in to earn continuing education units is approved by the _____ that requires the units.

Critical Thinking Scenarios

Read each scenario. Think about the information presented in the text, and then answer each question.

1. Brett recently graduated from a nursing program, passed his exams to become a registered nurse, and is working in the emergency room at a big-city hospital in his hometown.

   A. Which recent changes in society and health care are likely to affect his career as a nurse?

   _____

   _____

   _____

   B. What can Brett do throughout his career to keep current and respond to changes?

   _____

   _____

   _____

2. Sanjay is a radiographer. His wife recently returned to school and he is taking over more of the household duties and childcare responsibilities for the couple's three children.

   A. How can Sanjay ensure that he has necessary units for maintaining his state license?

   _____

   _____

   _____

   B. What are some efficient ways that Sanjay can earn the continuing education units needed to maintain his license?

   _____

   _____

   _____

© 2012 Cengage Learning. All Rights Reserved. May not be scanned, copied or duplicated, or posted to a publicly accessible website, in whole or in part.

UNIT 6
Communication in the Health Care Setting

© 2012 Cengage Learning. All Rights Reserved. May not be scanned, copied or duplicated, or posted to a publicly accessible website, in whole or in part.

CHAPTER 15

The Patient as an Individual

LEARNING OBJECTIVES

Studying and applying the material in this chapter will help you to:

■ Explain the meaning of the philosophy of individual worth and how it applies to work in health care.

■ Define *culture* and describe how it influences all aspects of human beliefs and behavior.

■ Give examples of how different cultural groups approach issues of health.

■ Describe how to determine the effect of cultural influences on the needs of patients.

■ List the five levels of Maslow's hierarchy of needs and give an example of each.

■ Recognize common defense mechanisms encountered in health care situations.

■ Explain how the health care professional can help patients deal with the experience of loss.

VOCABULARY REVIEW

Matching 1

Match the following terms with their correct definitions.

——— 1.	defense mechanism	A.	belief that every human being has value
——— 2.	Maslow's hierarchy of needs	B.	a person's view of himself or herself
——— 3.	philosophy of individual worth	C.	unconscious psychological responses to threatening or uncomfortable situations
——— 4.	physiological needs	D.	a high-level human need to achieve one's potential
——— 5.	self-actualization	E.	a visual representation that ranks human needs
——— 6.	self-esteem	F.	physical requirements for maintaining life

© 2012 Cengage Learning. All Rights Reserved. May not be scanned, copied or duplicated, or posted to a publicly accessible website, in whole or in part.

Word Fill

Complete the following sentences by filling in the missing words.

personal space   dominant culture   shamans   culture
prejudice

1. _____ is the term that means the values, shared beliefs, and customs of a group of people.

2. The fundamental beliefs about what is considered by most people to be ideal behavior is a society's _____.

3. The appropriate distance that a given group of people consider appropriate for carrying on a conversation is known as _____.

4. If John has negative feelings about a classmate simply because she belongs to a certain ethnic group, John is demonstrating _____.

5. Traditional healers, known as _____, receive a calling and are believed to communicate with the spirits.

CHAPTER REVIEW

True/False

Indicate whether the following statements are true (T) or false (F).

_____ 1. It is not necessary to show special consideration to patients who are rude and uncooperative.

_____ 2. Almost everyone has prejudices of some kind.

_____ 3. It is not necessary to agree with the cultural beliefs of patients about health.

_____ 4. It is not necessary to learn about the culture of your patients because they will be treated with the best that Western medicine has to offer.

_____ 5. If you explain self-care procedures carefully, patients will understand and follow your instructions.

_____ 6. Most cultures today respect the importance of being on time and using time efficiently.

_____ 7. In some cultures it is considered rude not to inquire about one's family.

_____ 8. In the United States, the appropriate distance between two people who are conversing is about 18 inches.

_____ 9. It is best not to assume that just because a person speaks some English, he or she will understand everything you say.

_____ 10. Most cultures consider illness to be physically based.

© 2012 Cengage Learning. All Rights Reserved. May not be scanned, copied or duplicated, or posted to a publicly accessible website, in whole or in part.

—— 11. Religious and spiritual beliefs influence the health care beliefs of many people in the United States.

—— 12. It is reported that about 25 percent of people in the United States use prayer to assist them with healing.

—— 13. *Humors* are body fluids that the members of some cultures believe control the health of the body.

—— 14. Because they are natural, herbs are much safer to use for medicinal purposes than pharmaceutical drugs.

—— 15. Natural, plant-based remedies are not regulated by the Food and Drug Administration.

Matching 2

Match the following defense mechanisms with their correct definitions.

—— 1. compensation

A. retaining unpleasant thoughts and memories subconsciously

—— 2. control

B. faking illness to avoid something

—— 3. denial

C. taking charge in an inappropriate situation when unable to do so in another

—— 4. displacement

D. redirecting strong feelings about one person to someone else

—— 5. malingering

E. demonstrating behaviors inappropriate for one's age

—— 6. projection

F. offering an acceptable, but untrue, reason for one's behavior

—— 7. rationalization

G. shutting off contact with others

—— 8. regression

H. placing blame for one's own weaknesses onto someone else

—— 9. repression

I. doing something unsuitable in an attempt to meet a need

—— 10. withdrawal

J. pretending that something unpleasant is not true

Short Answer

Read each question. Think about the information presented in the text, and then answer each question.

1. What are three major factors that combine to make up an individual?

_____

_____

_____

_____

© 2012 Cengage Learning. All Rights Reserved. May not be scanned, copied or duplicated, or posted to a publicly accessible website, in whole or in part.

2. What are five appropriate questions to ask patients to learn about their health care beliefs so you can treat them as individuals?

_____

_____

_____

_____

3. What are five beliefs that various cultures have about the source of good health?

_____

_____

_____

_____

4. List nine beliefs held by people of different backgrounds about the cause of illness.

_____

_____

_____

_____

5. What are the five levels of needs proposed by Maslow in his hierarchy of needs? List them in order beginning with the lowest level.

_____

_____

_____

_____

6. What are five common ways that individuals deal with loss, such as a serious health problem or the death of a spouse?

_____

_____

_____

_____

7. What are four ways that health care professionals can help patients who appear to be demonstrating defense mechanisms feel less threatened?

_____

_____

_____

_____

8. What are five ways that health care professionals can help patients preserve or increase their self-esteem?

_____

_____

_____

_____

9. Explain how the concept of time differs between various cultural groups.

_____

_____

_____

_____

10. What is the meaning of *personal space*?

_____

_____

_____

_____

Completion

Use the words in the list to complete the following statements:

direct eye contact	faith healing	yin and yang	philosophy of human worth
acupuncture	prejudice	stress	ancestral spirits
t'ai chi	personal space		

1. The concept that every human being has value and should be treated with respect is called the _____.

2. Drawing a conclusion about a person because he belongs to a certain ethnic group is an example of _____.

3. _____ , a series of movements originally developed for self-defense, has health benefits that include improved flexibility and balance.

4. An important concept in Chinese medicine is that illness occurs when _____ is/are out of balance.

5. Controlling the flow of body energy by inserting tiny needles into the skin is called _____.

6. Standing too close to another person when speaking shows a lack of understanding of the concept of _____.

© 2012 Cengage Learning. All Rights Reserved. May not be scanned, copied or duplicated, or posted to a publicly accessible website, in whole or in part.

7. In some cultures, touching the head is distressing because it is the home of _____.

8. _____ is a sign of aggression or a lack of respect in some cultures.

9. _____ is based on the belief that illness can be cured by prayer and strong religious beliefs.

10. Practitioners of traditional Western medicine are recognizing the close connection of the mind and body, especially the effects of _____ on the body.

Critical Thinking Scenarios

Read each scenario. Think about the information presented in the text, and then answer each question.

1. James Dixon has called Dr. Adler's office a number of times in the last couple of months complaining of various symptoms. Dr. Adler always sees James and has noted that each time, the symptoms are different. To date, he cannot identify what might be causing this variety of symptoms. James always asks Dr. Adler to write an excuse for his employer and on his last visit he mentioned to the doctor that, "It doesn't really matter if I show up or not, my supervisor hates me."

   A. What are two defense mechanisms that James might be displaying?

   _____
   _____
   _____

   B. How do defense mechanisms help individuals deal with difficult situations?

   _____
   _____
   _____

   C. How might defense mechanisms be helping James deal with his work situation?

   _____
   _____
   _____

2. Claire Mason is an 88-year-old woman who recently entered a long-term care facility. Her family does not live in the area and she is feeling sad and depressed.

   A. What are possible reasons for Claire's feelings of sadness and depression?

   _____
   _____
   _____

   B. How can the nurses in the facility help Claire meet her needs for love and affection?

   _____
   _____

© 2012 Cengage Learning. All Rights Reserved. May not be scanned, copied or duplicated, or posted to a publicly accessible website, in whole or in part.

CHAPTER 16

The Communication Process

LEARNING OBJECTIVES

Studying and applying the material in this chapter will help you to:

- Explain the importance of effective communication in health care.
- Describe the relationship between effective communication and patient well-being.
- List and describe the six steps of the communication process.
- Define and explain the use of the four types of questions.
- Explain the meaning of nonverbal communication and give examples of three types.
- Explain the meaning of *active listening*.
- Define *empathy* and explain its application in health care.
- Explain the meaning of *feedback* and how it is used in communication.
- Recognize common barriers that can prevent effective communication.
- List the techniques to use when communicating with patients who have special needs.
- Demonstrate professional telephone techniques and explain why it is important to apply them in the health care facility.
- Describe the elements that make up effective patient education.
- List strategies for preparing and giving presentations to groups.
- List three ways to handle situations that involve gossip.

© 2012 Cengage Learning. All Rights Reserved. May not be scanned, copied or duplicated, or posted to a publicly accessible website, in whole or in part.

VOCABULARY REVIEW

Definitions

Write the definition of each of the following words or terms.

1. empathy

   _____

   _____

   _____

2. feedback

   _____

   _____

   _____

3. learning objectives

   _____

   _____

   _____

4. sympathy

   _____

   _____

   _____

Matching 1

Match the following terms with their correct definitions.

_____ 1. closed-ended	A.	feedback technique to request additional information to illustrate the speaker's meaning
_____ 2. leading	B.	type of question that includes part of the answer
_____ 3. open-ended	C.	feedback technique in which listeners state what they hear in their own words
_____ 4. paraphrasing	D.	type of question that can be answered with one word
_____ 5. probing	E.	type of question that asks for additional information or clarification
_____ 6. reflecting	F.	type of question that must be answered with more than a one-word response
_____ 7. requesting examples	G.	feedback technique that prompts speakers to complete or add information to their original messages

© 2012 Cengage Learning. All Rights Reserved. May not be scanned, copied or duplicated, or posted to a publicly accessible website, in whole or in part.

Word Fill

Complete the following sentences by filling in the missing words.

barriers	nonverbal communication	active listening	sender
pantomime	receiver	communication	

1. _____ is characterized by focusing your full attention on what a speaker is saying.

2. _____ that block communication include conditions such as noise and hearing impairments.

3. The process of sending and receiving messages is called _____.

4. Information exchanged without the use of words involves _____.

5. _____ can be an effective way of conveying meaning through acting out and gestures with patients who do not understand English.

6. Another word for the listener in a communication exchange is the _____.

7. The _____ is the person communicating a message.

CHAPTER REVIEW

True/False

Indicate whether the following statements are true (T) or false (F).

_____ 1. The ability to communicate well is as important as good technical skills.

_____ 2. Using casual words such as "you know" is a good way to put patients at ease.

_____ 3. If a patient hesitates briefly when answering a question, it is recommended that the health care professional help by suggesting answers.

_____ 4. Humor is usually not appropriate with patients who are ill or injured.

_____ 5. Many patients who cannot speak and appear unresponsive can hear and experience touch.

_____ 6. Nonverbal communication conveys about 70 percent of a spoken message.

_____ 7. Greeting patients with names such as "dear" and "sweetie" is a good way to make them feel comfortable.

_____ 8. Feeling and expressing sympathy is a good way for the health care professional to better understand a patient.

_____ 9. The meaning of gestures varies among cultural groups and must be used with care.

_____ 10. The ability to listen is as important for health care professionals as the ability to explain clearly.

_____ 11. Periods of silence during communication are uncomfortable for both parties and should be avoided.

© 2012 Cengage Learning. All Rights Reserved. May not be scanned, copied or duplicated, or posted to a publicly accessible website, in whole or in part.

_____ 12. Patients who are facing death generally prefer to be left alone.

_____ 13. Nearly half of all adults age 75 and older have some form of hearing impairment.

_____ 14. It is recommended that when faced with an angry patient, the health care professional should start by asking the individual to calm down.

_____ 15. Speaking loudly is not generally helpful when speaking to someone who has a hearing impairment or does not understand English well.

_____ 16. Confidential information regarding health matters cannot be left for patients on their telephone answering machines.

_____ 17. Planning ahead and organizing what you are going to say is really only necessary when addressing large groups of people.

_____ 18. It is acceptable to gossip about others if they are not present and there is no chance they will hear what you have said.

_____ 19. Patient information should never be discussed during social conversations.

_____ 20. Patients generally do not mind if you discuss their condition in front of them with other health care professionals.

Matching 2

Match the following terms with the examples that best illustrate them.

_____ 1. closed-ended   A. can you tell me more about when you experience this pain?

_____ 2. open-ended   B. what is your age?

_____ 3. probing   C. what kinds of foods seem to make your tooth hurt?

_____ 4. leading   D. does your tooth hurt most when you are eating something cold?

_____ 5. paraphrasing   E. I'd like to listen and see if I can understand how you're feeling about this.

_____ 6. reflecting   F. am I hearing you say that the medicine doesn't seem to be helping?

_____ 7. requesting example   G. I'm really not comfortable talking about Roy when he's not here.

_____ 8. empathy   H. when we are finished, you will be able to dress the wound properly.

_____ 9. learning objective   I. what are your plans for the future?

_____ 10. response to gossip   J. you told me you've been taking this medication for your diabetes for …

© 2012 Cengage Learning. All Rights Reserved. May not be scanned, copied or duplicated, or posted to a publicly accessible website, in whole or in part.

Short Answer

Read each question. Think about the information presented in the text, and then answer each question.

1. What are four trends in health care delivery that have increased the need for good communication skills?

_____

_____

_____

2. How does good communication influence patient well-being?

_____

_____

_____

3. List the six steps in the communication process.

_____

_____

_____

4. What are five factors the health care professional should consider to determine a patient's level of understanding when planning communication goals?

_____

_____

_____

5. Give five organizational strategies you can use when creating long messages so they are easy for the listener to follow.

_____

_____

_____

6. Give six examples of positive body language that may encourage patients to share information.

_____

_____

_____

7. State the pros and cons of using touch with patients.

_____

_____

_____

© 2012 Cengage Learning. All Rights Reserved. May not be scanned, copied or duplicated, or posted to a publicly accessible website, in whole or in part.

8. What are eight characteristics of good listening skills?

    _____

    _____

    _____

9. List five examples of communication barriers commonly encountered in health care settings.

    _____

    _____

    _____

10. What are ten actions you can take to more effectively communicate with patients who are in pain?

    _____

    _____

    _____

11. What are eight techniques to use when communicating with individuals who have hearing impairments?

    _____

    _____

    _____

12. What are five techniques to use when communicating with individuals who have visual impairments?

    _____

    _____

    _____

Ordering

Place the following steps for delivering patient education in the order in which they should be performed. Put a numeral 1 before the first step, a 2 before the next, and so on.

_____ 1. Listen

_____ 2. Create the instructional message

_____ 3. Set educational goals

_____ 4. Deliver the instruction

_____ 5. Evaluate

_____ 6. Check for understanding

© 2012 Cengage Learning. All Rights Reserved. May not be scanned, copied or duplicated, or posted to a publicly accessible website, in whole or in part.

Completion

Use the words in the list to complete the following statements:

telephone	nonverbal communication	hearing impairments	disoriented
barriers	smile	active listening	needs
gossip	patient education		

1. Physical distractions and sensory impairments can present _____ to communication.

2. The first contact that many patients have with a health care facility is by _____.

3. Focusing on what another person is saying is a characteristic of _____.

4. Eye contact and leaning toward the speaker are examples of _____.

5. Proper nutrition and back strengthening exercises are examples of topics for _____.

6. _____ has no purpose and should not be allowed in the health care workplace.

7. Make sure there is a light source on your face when speaking with patients who have _____.

8. Identify yourself and say the patient's name when you are communicating with a patient who is _____.

9. When speaking to a group about a health topic, plan ahead and identify the _____ of the audience.

10. A/an _____ is a universal sign of good will.

© 2012 Cengage Learning. All Rights Reserved. May not be scanned, copied or duplicated, or posted to a publicly accessible website, in whole or in part.

Critical Thinking Scenarios

Read each scenario. Think about the information presented in the text, and then answer each question.

1. Carla works at the front desk of a busy urgent care clinic. Her job is to answer the phones and greet patients, learning enough about each to determine in what order they should see the physicians.

   A. What can Carla do to make patients, who sometimes have to wait for her attention, feel welcome and attended to?

   _____

   _____

   _____

   B. What are guidelines she can follow to ensure that her telephone manner is welcoming and professional and that her speech is easy to understand?

   _____

   _____

   _____

2. Jorge is the clinical medical assistant for a plastic surgeon who performs many in-office procedures. Part of his job is to provide pre- and post-operative patient education.

   A. How does patient education influence patient recovery from surgery?

   _____

   _____

   _____

   B. What should Jorge's first step be when delivering patient education?

   _____

   _____

   _____

   C. How can he check to ensure that a patient has understood his instructions?

   _____

   _____

   _____

© 2012 Cengage Learning. All Rights Reserved. May not be scanned, copied or duplicated, or posted to a publicly accessible website, in whole or in part.

CHAPTER 18

Computers and Technology in Health Care

LEARNING OBJECTIVES

Studying and applying the material in this chapter will help you to:

- Explain why it is important for today's health care professional to be computer literate.

- Describe how computers and technology are applied in the following areas of health care:

  - Information management
  - Creation of documents
  - Electronic medical records
  - Numerical calculations
  - Diagnostics
  - Treatment
  - Patient monitoring
  - Research
  - Education
  - Communication

- Explain the difference between computer hardware and software.

- Describe how to properly handle and maintain hardware components.

- Identify and describe the two major types of data storage.

- List six important guidelines for using computers effectively.

- Explain precautions that the health care professional can take to ensure computer security.

- List ways that the health care professional can acquire computer skills.

© 2012 Cengage Learning. All Rights Reserved. May not be scanned, copied or duplicated, or posted to a publicly accessible website, in whole or in part.

VOCABULARY REVIEW

Definitions

Write the definition of each of the following words or terms.

1. bioinformatics

   _____

   _____

   _____

2. computer literate

   _____

   _____

   _____

3. plagiarism

   _____

   _____

   _____

4. point of care charting

   _____

   _____

   _____

5. site license

   _____

   _____

   _____

6. style manual

   _____

   _____

   _____

© 2012 Cengage Learning. All Rights Reserved. May not be scanned, copied or duplicated, or posted to a publicly accessible website, in whole or in part.

Matching 1

Match the following terms with their correct definitions.

_____ 1. CD-ROM

_____ 2. central processing unit

_____ 3. fiber optics

_____ 4. hard drive

_____ 5. hardware

_____ 6. lasers

_____ 7. networks

_____ 8. peripherals

_____ 9. RAM

A. focused light rays that can cut and remove tissue

B. workspace in the computer that stores data while the computer is turned on

C. component of the computer that manages and performs operations

D. linked computers that communicate and share data

E. permanent data storage device

F. devices attached to computers

G. optical disk that stores data

H. physical components of a computer

I. technology in which data are transmitted via thin cables

Matching 2

Match the following terms with their correct definitions.

_____ 1. download

_____ 2. electronic mail

_____ 3. gateways

_____ 4. Internet

_____ 5. key words

_____ 6. search engine

_____ 7. telemedicine

_____ 8. virtual communities

_____ 9. virus (computer)

_____ 10. Web directories

A. creating and sending messages from one computer to another

B. worldwide system of networked computers

C. groups of individuals who use the Internet to communicate and share information

D. software program that searches for and retrieves documents from the Internet

E. lists of and links to Web pages

F. websites that serve mainly to provide links to other websites

G. to transfer files from the Internet onto one's computer

H. practice of medicine via phone lines

I. term or phrase used to search for specific information on the Web

J. software that contains instructions to perform destructive operations

© 2012 Cengage Learning. All Rights Reserved. May not be scanned, copied or duplicated, or posted to a publicly accessible website, in whole or in part.

Word Fill

Complete the following sentences by filling in the missing words.

artificial intelligence	electronic spreadsheets	software	record
application programs	database	files	fields
expert systems			

1. Word processing software and antivirus programs are examples of _____.

2. Technology that enables computers to make decisions that we previously believed could be made only by humans is called _____.

3. Organizing data in structured ways so they can be easily accessed can be done with _____ software.

4. _____ enable(s) users to perform numerical calculations.

5. Specialized collections of computerized data that assist physicians in diagnostics and treatments are called _____.

6. _____ are categories set up in a database to help organize information.

7. Groups of related computerized records are called _____.

8. The term for describing a collection of related data is a/an _____.

9. Without _____ , a computer is like a disk player without a disk, unable to perform any operations.

CHAPTER REVIEW

True/False

Indicate whether the following statements are true (T) or false (F).

_____ 1. Most health care facilities in the United States have a comprehensive electronic records system in place.

_____ 2. Software is now available that converts spoken words to text.

_____ 3. Health care professionals who provide direct patient care, such as nurses, have very few tasks that require using a computer.

_____ 4. The federal government is encouraging the use of electronic medical records to increase efficiency and decrease the cost of health care.

_____ 5. Submitting Medicare claims electronically is voluntary.

_____ 6. Some physicians are concerned that electronic medical records are subject to errors and may compromise patient care.

© 2012 Cengage Learning. All Rights Reserved. May not be scanned, copied or duplicated, or posted to a publicly accessible website, in whole or in part.

—— 7. Reports created from voice dictation software are nearly as accurate as reports transcribed from written documents.

—— 8. Database software is helpful for exploring future scenarios, such as how many physical therapists to hire for a new rehabilitation hospital.

—— 9. New tracking methods have reduced adverse reactions to prescription drugs to nearly zero.

—— 10. It is illegal for employers to check activity on workplace computers, including e-mails, of their employees.

Matching 3

Match the following terms with the short descriptions.

—— 1. antivirus software

—— 2. laptops

—— 3. personal interface

—— 4. password

—— 5. RAM

—— 6. virtual communities

—— 7. site license

—— 8. download

—— 9. mailing lists

—— 10. telepharmacies

—— 11. application programs

—— 12. HIPAA

A. allow the dispensing of drugs at off-site locations

B. provides means of communication between homebound individuals

C. automatically distribute e-mails on specific topics

D. consist of CPU and peripherals in one unit

E. enable computer to perform specialized tasks

F. temporarily stores information in the computer

G. gives permission to install software on more than one computer

H. prevents destructive instructions from invading your computer

I. legislation that addresses the privacy of medical records

J. when creating this, do not choose something obvious

K. never do this with files if you don't know who sent them

L. health care professionals need to provide this between patients and computers

© 2012 Cengage Learning. All Rights Reserved. May not be scanned, copied or duplicated, or posted to a publicly accessible website, in whole or in part.

Short Answer

Read each question. Think about the information presented in the text, and then answer each question.

1. What are the three major types of operations performed by computers?

    _____

    _____

    _____

2. Why is it important for health care professionals to be computer literate?

    _____

    _____

    _____

3. What does it mean when a health care professional is *computer literate*?

    _____

    _____

    _____

4. What were the goals of the Human Genome Project?

    _____

    _____

    _____

5. List six recommendations for the care and maintenance of computer equipment.

    _____

    _____

    _____

6. What does MEDLINE, maintained by the National Library of Medicine, contain?

    _____

    _____

    _____

7. How have computers decreased the time needed for obtaining the Food and Drug Administration's approval of new pharmaceutical products?

    _____

    _____

    _____

© 2012 Cengage Learning. All Rights Reserved. May not be scanned, copied or duplicated, or posted to a publicly accessible website, in whole or in part.

8. How does virtual reality technology enable surgeons to perform better?

_____

_____

_____

9. What is featured on the Medline Plus website?

_____

_____

_____

10. List six guidelines for evaluating the reliability of a website.

_____

_____

_____

Critical Thinking Scenarios

Read each scenario. Think about the information presented in the text, and then answer each question.

1. Ed had an appointment with Dr. Cardoza today about pain he's been experiencing in his abdomen. Dr. Cardoza noted a lump in Ed's abdomen and is arranging for him to have an MRI. On the way out of the office, Ed expressed concerns about the procedure to Addison, Dr. Cardoza's medical assistant.

   A. Why might Dr. Cardoza have recommended an MRI?

   _____

   _____

   _____

   B. What happens during the procedure?

   _____

   _____

   _____

   C. How can Addison help Ed feel more comfortable about having an MRI?

   _____

   _____

   _____

© 2012 Cengage Learning. All Rights Reserved. May not be scanned, copied or duplicated, or posted to a publicly accessible website, in whole or in part.

2. Jeb is a newly graduated surgical technologist. He wants to learn more about the developing field of robotics and how they are used in surgery.

   A. Where might he locate the most current information?

   _____

   _____

   _____

   B. What key words might be useful for finding information on the Internet?

   _____

   _____

   _____

   C. What types of websites generally have the most reliable information?

   _____

   _____

   _____

Completion

Use the words in the list to complete the following statements:

computed tomography	expert system	determine brain function	fiber optics
lasers	electronic chip	electrical impedance tomography	robotic surgery
image-guided	magnetic resonance imaging	sound waves	artificial intelligence

1. The diagnostic technique that takes X-rays from various angles and is used to evaluate soft tissue is called _____.

2. A common use of this diagnostic tool in which a radioactive substance is injected into the patient is to _____.

3. _____ is an experimental diagnostic technique in which electrodes are attached to the patient's skin.

4. The activity of hydrogen atoms in tissues is the basis for _____.

5. ATHENA is an example of a/an _____.

6. Ultrasonography uses _____ in place of X-rays to create images of organs and abnormalities.

© 2012 Cengage Learning. All Rights Reserved. May not be scanned, copied or duplicated, or posted to a publicly accessible website, in whole or in part.

7. Some dentists use computer technology by placing a/an _____ in the patient's mouth to send an image to a computer.

8. Hair-thin cables transmit data in a technology called _____.

9. The sophisticated technology that helps health care professionals make decisions is _____.

10. Cameras that provide high-resolution, three-dimensional images are used to perform _____.

11. Highly focused light rays, called _____, are now used to make precise cuts in tissue.

12. _____ surgery is very accurate because it is based on a three-dimensional mapping system and technology that reports the exact location of surgical instruments.

© 2012 Cengage Learning. All Rights Reserved. May not be scanned, copied or duplicated, or posted to a publicly accessible website, in whole or in part.

CHAPTER 19

Documentation and Medical Records

LEARNING OBJECTIVES

Studying and applying the material in this chapter will help you to:

- List and explain the purposes of medical documentation.
- List the characteristics of good medical documentation.
- Explain the proper method for correcting errors on medical records.
- List the various sources of information that may be found in a medical record.
- Describe three different formats used for progress notes.
- Discuss the advantages and disadvantages of each progress note format.

© 2012 Cengage Learning. All Rights Reserved. May not be scanned, copied or duplicated, or posted to a publicly accessible website, in whole or in part.

VOCABULARY REVIEW

Matching 1

Match the following terms with their correct definitions.

_____ 1. assessment

_____ 2. charting

_____ 3. chief complaint

_____ 4. medical documentation

_____ 5. medical history

_____ 6. medical record

_____ 7. plan

_____ 8. progress notes

_____ 9. SOAP

A. recording observations and information about patients

B. a format for charting that uses a problem-oriented approach

C. gathering information; a step in charting that is the health care professional's impression of what is wrong with the patient, based on the signs and symptoms

D. written chronological statements about a patient's care

E. the patient's statement of the main reason he or she is seeking medical care

F. a step in SOAP charting that documents the procedures, treatments, and patient instructions that make up the patient's care

G. notes and documents that health care professionals add to the medical record

H. the collection of all documents that are filed together and form a complete chronological health history of a particular patient

I. data collected on a patient that includes personal, familial, and social information

CHAPTER REVIEW

True/False

Indicate whether the following statements are true (T) or false (F).

_____ 1. An example of medical documentation would be patient statistics and information about care.

_____ 2. Charting is the process of administering care.

_____ 3. A medical record refers to a section of personal notes made by the physician only.

_____ 4. Many health care professionals are responsible for some aspect of charting.

_____ 5. Patient comments should not be included in a medical record; only observations made by health care professional should be included.

© 2012 Cengage Learning. All Rights Reserved. May not be scanned, copied or duplicated, or posted to a publicly accessible website, in whole or in part.

_____ 6. Complete and accurate medical documentation is critical in providing consistent patient care.

_____ 7. Information included in the medical record is a significant source of data on which other health care professionals can base their approach to the patient.

_____ 8. The medical record is not a legal document and as such cannot be used in a court of law.

_____ 9. The security of records is the responsibility of each health care professional.

_____ 10. The progress notes make up the written record of every aspect of a patient's relationship with the health care professional.

_____ 11. Computers are being increasingly used in the health care field.

_____ 12. Electronic medical records (EMR) offer less options for information than core charting.

_____ 13. The computerized systems can also include many informational and safety tools.

_____ 14. Personal health records (PHR) are becoming increasingly important due to the mobility of individuals and frequent changes in health care providers.

_____ 15. HIPAA is a private accreditation agency that makes site visits to facilities.

Matching 2

Match the following terms with their correct definitions.

_____ 1. source-oriented record format

A. forms for specialty needs

_____ 2. continuous chronological record format

B. record is divided into different sections by specialty

_____ 3. familial history

C. when the primary physician asks another physician to see the patient

_____ 4. social history

D. if and how much patient smokes, drinks alcohol, or takes illegal drugs

_____ 5. personal history

E. when the physician dictates findings and then they are typed from the taped message

_____ 6. consultation

F. all documentation organized by date entered

_____ 7. transcription services

G. patient's past medical problems and surgeries, allergies, etc.

_____ 8. flow sheets

H. includes all medications administered by health care professionals at the facility

_____ 9. medication record

I. medical problems of relatives

_____ 10. progress notes

J. written chronological statements about a patient's care

© 2012 Cengage Learning. All Rights Reserved. May not be scanned, copied or duplicated, or posted to a publicly accessible website, in whole or in part.

Short Answer

Read each question. Think about the information presented in the text, and then answer each question.

1. List the characteristics of good medical documentation.

   _____

   _____

   _____

2. What does it mean when it is stated that charting needs to be clearly and objectively expressed?

   _____

   _____

   _____

3. Why is it important that the health care professional uses correct spelling, terminology, punctuation, and grammar when charting?

   _____

   _____

   _____

4. When should charting be completed? Why?

   _____

   _____

   _____

5. When is the appropriate time to chart a medication or procedure?

   _____

   _____

   _____

6. What are the proper steps to take when correcting a written documentation?

   _____

   _____

   _____

7. Give an example of when a flow sheet may be used.

   _____

   _____

   _____

© 2012 Cengage Learning. All Rights Reserved. May not be scanned, copied or duplicated, or posted to a publicly accessible website, in whole or in part.

8. What are graphic forms used for?

_____

_____

_____

9. What are diagnostic tests?

_____

_____

_____

10. What is included in physician's orders?

_____

_____

_____

Completion

Use the words in the list to complete the following statements:

"thinning the chart"	done	subjective	JCAHO
medical history	objective	problem-oriented	narrative
evaluation	charting by exception (CBE)		

1. Only through written documentation can tests, procedures, and treatment be proven to have occurred. In the world of health care, "If it isn't documented, it isn't _____."

2. _____ is an accreditation organization for health care facilities.

3. A/An _____ includes the personal, familial, and social history of a patient.

4. _____ is done when the chart becomes too thick and another file on the patient is started.

5. _____ medical records are organized around the patient's health problems.

6. _____ information is that which is sensed and reported by the patient.

7. _____ information includes observations of health care professionals.

8. A/An _____ is done to determine what the results were and if the treatment was effective.

9. _____ charting includes detailed written notes on all aspects of care.

10. _____ is an abbreviated chart format where only abnormal findings are noted.

© 2012 Cengage Learning. All Rights Reserved. May not be scanned, copied or duplicated, or posted to a publicly accessible website, in whole or in part.

Critical Thinking Scenarios

Read each scenario. Think about the information presented in the text, and then answer each question.

1. Mrs. Gonzales comes into the clinic and says her husband asked her to stop by to get information as to when his next appointment is scheduled.

    A. Can this information be given to Mrs. Gonzales?

    _____

    _____

    _____

    B. Why or why not?

    _____

    _____

    _____

    C. What are the possible consequences if correct protocol is not followed?

    _____

    _____

    _____

2. Ms. Sally Jessups has read an article about creating a personal health record. She wonders if this is something she should put together.

    A. What reasons might she want to consider in her decision?

    _____

    _____

    _____

    B. What type of information should this record include?

    _____

    _____

    _____

    C. What are the advantages of having a personal health record?

    _____

    _____

    _____

© 2012 Cengage Learning. All Rights Reserved. May not be scanned, copied or duplicated, or posted to a publicly accessible website, in whole or in part.

UNIT 7
Health Care Skills

© 2012 Cengage Learning. All Rights Reserved. May not be scanned, copied or duplicated, or posted to a publicly accessible website, in whole or in part.

CHAPTER 20

Physical Assessment

LEARNING OBJECTIVES

Studying and applying the material in this chapter will help you to:

- State the purpose of a "History and Physical" and indicate what data the physician will obtain.

- Discuss variances from the norm for each of the body systems.

- Explain how to do a pain scale assessment.

- Define what is included in assessment of the activities of daily living (ADLs).

- Correctly take the vital signs (temperature, pulse, respirations, and blood pressure).

- Describe how the presence of an apical-radial deficit is determined and what it means.

- Measure the height and weight of a patient.

© 2012 Cengage Learning. All Rights Reserved. May not be scanned, copied or duplicated, or posted to a publicly accessible website, in whole or in part.

VOCABULARY REVIEW

Matching 1

Match the following terms with their correct definitions.

_____ 1. afebrile

_____ 2. apnea

_____ 3. bradycardia

_____ 4. bradypnea

_____ 5. Cheyne-Stokes

_____ 6. dyspnea

_____ 7. eupnea

_____ 8. exhalation

_____ 9. hypertension

_____ 10. hypotension

_____ 11. inhalation

A. a respiratory rate that is below the normal range

B. breathing that is within the normal range, is unlabored, and has an even rhythm

C. blood pressure below the normal range

D. absence of respirations

E. a temperature that is within the normal range

F. blood pressure above the normal range

G. the part of the respiratory cycle when air enters the lungs

H. the part of the respiratory cycle when air is removed from the lungs

I. a heart rate that is below the normal rate

J. a breathing pattern that has a period of apnea followed by a gradually increasing depth and frequency of respirations

K. labored breathing or difficulty with breathing

© 2012 Cengage Learning. All Rights Reserved. May not be scanned, copied or duplicated, or posted to a publicly accessible website, in whole or in part.

Matching 2

Match the following definitions with their correct terms.

—— 1. the process of taking air into and removing air from the lungs

A. febrile

—— 2. a temperature that is elevated above the normal range

B. orthopnea

—— 3. an instrument that amplifies sounds so they can be heard from within the body

C. orthostatic (postural) hypotension

—— 4. when a patient has difficulty breathing unless in a sitting or standing position

D. pulse deficit

—— 5. a heart rate that is above the normal range

E. pulse points

—— 6. the difference between a pulse point and an apical rate that are taken simultaneously

F. respiration

—— 7. an instrument that records the blood pressure

G. stethoscope

—— 8. a respiratory rate that is above the normal range

H. sphygmomanometer

—— 9. the rapid lowering of the blood pressure as a result of changing positions

I. tachycardia

—— 10. measuring the blood pressure, temperature, pulse, and respiration to give some indication of how the body is functioning

J. tachypnea

—— 11. specific sites on the body where arterial pulsations can be felt

K. vital signs

© 2012 Cengage Learning. All Rights Reserved. May not be scanned, copied or duplicated, or posted to a publicly accessible website, in whole or in part.

CHAPTER REVIEW

Identification

Place an "X" in front of the items of information that are included in the patient's H&P.

_____ 1. demographic date

_____ 2. date

_____ 3. chief complaint

_____ 4. history of present illness

_____ 5. current health status

_____ 6. criminal record

_____ 7. source of referral

_____ 8. family history of illness

_____ 9. review of all systems

_____ 10. psychosocial history

True/False Rewrite

Please rewrite the bold part of the sentence to make the statement true.

1. The **admission office personnel** takes a history and performs a physical on patients when they are seen for the first time or when they are admitted to the hospital.

   _____

   _____

   _____

2. Demographic data include **general state of the patient's health**.

   _____

   _____

   _____

3. A referral source is a **list of all prior hospitalizations**.

   _____

   _____

   _____

4. A chief complaint is the primary problem from the **physician's view** as to why they are seeking medical care.

   _____

   _____

   _____

© 2012 Cengage Learning. All Rights Reserved. May not be scanned, copied or duplicated, or posted to a publicly accessible website, in whole or in part.

5. The observational skills needed are based on a thorough understanding of **etiology and pathophysiology**.

_____

_____

_____

6. **Percussion** refers to the use of the senses of vision, hearing, and smell for observation of patient condition.

_____

_____

_____

7. A patient's gait refers to **the status of his or her skin.**

_____

_____

_____

8. Assessing capillary refill is when the health care professional **inspects the neck veins for distention.**

_____

_____

_____

9. Menarche means **menopause.**

_____

_____

_____

10. An axillary temperature will be a **higher** than an oral temperature.

_____

_____

_____

Multiple Choice

Circle the best answer for each of the following questions. There is only one correct answer to each question.

1. Which of the following mean a temperature is elevated above the normal range?
   A. febrile
   B. afebrile
   C. intermittent fever

© 2012 Cengage Learning. All Rights Reserved. May not be scanned, copied or duplicated, or posted to a publicly accessible website, in whole or in part.

2. What creates pulsing sensation felt by health care professionals at certain points in the body?

    A. the coronary arteries contracting
    B. the heart valves opening
    C. the heart contracting

3. What is the name of the type of pulse being taken when a stethoscope is used to listen to the heart beat?

    A. carotid
    B. apical
    C. radial

4. What creates the sound of "lub dub" heard when a stethoscope is placed over the heart?

    A. heart contracting
    B. valves closing
    C. flow of blood

5. What is the normal range for the pulse of an adult?

    A. 60–80 beats per minute
    B. 60–90 beats per minute
    C. 80–100 beats per minute

6. If the apical pulse if 90 and the radial pulse is 50, what is the pulse deficit?

    A. 40
    B. 50
    C. 90

7. What is the normal respiratory range for an adult?

    A. 22–34 breaths per minute
    B. 18–24 breaths per minute
    C. 16–20 breaths per minute

8. Which number is the diastolic if the blood pressure is 134/76 and the pulse is 84?

    A. 134
    B. 76
    C. 84

9. What is white coat syndrome?

    A. when a patient wants to make their own diagnosis
    B. an increased blood pressure during office visits
    C. a fear of white

10. Which of the following would be a reason not to use an arm for a blood pressure reading?

    A. Patient had mastectomy of that side
    B. Patient recently had abdominal surgery
    C. Patient recently had blood drawn in that arm

© 2012 Cengage Learning. All Rights Reserved. May not be scanned, copied or duplicated, or posted to a publicly accessible website, in whole or in part.

Short Answer

Read each question. Think about the information presented in the text, and then answer each question.

1. What is meant by doing a general survey and why is it done?

_____

_____

_____

2. What should be included in a psychosocial assessment?

_____

_____

_____

3. What are the skills frequently used during the physical assessment of the patient?

_____

_____

_____

4. Explain the two primary methods used to assess pain.

_____

_____

_____

5. What are ADLs?

_____

_____

_____

6. When taking a pulse, what three observations are made?

_____

_____

_____

7. When taking a respiratory rate, what three observations are made?

_____

_____

_____

8. How do vital signs vary over the life span?

_____

_____

_____

© 2012 Cengage Learning. All Rights Reserved. May not be scanned, copied or duplicated, or posted to a publicly accessible website, in whole or in part.

9. List the four methods commonly used to record a patient's weight.

_____

_____

_____

10. If you need a patient's height but he or she cannot stand, what do you do?

_____

_____

_____

Ordering 1

Place the following duties in the order in which they should be performed when doing a head-to-toe assessment on an adult. Put a numeral 1 before the first duty, a 2 before the next, and so on.

_____ 1. chest (respiratory and cardiac symptoms)

_____ 2. orientation

_____ 3. neck

_____ 4. head

_____ 5. abdomen

_____ 6. upper extremities

_____ 7. lower extremities

Ordering 2

Place the following duties in the order in which they should be performed when taking a manual blood pressure. Put a numeral 1 before the first duty, a 2 before the next, and so on.

_____ 1. Add 30 to the reading obtained in the prior step

_____ 2. Deflate cuff until can no longer hear any sounds

_____ 3. Locate brachial artery

_____ 4. Inflate cuff until cannot feel radial artery

_____ 5. Deflate cuff until hear first sound

_____ 6. Inflate cuff to predetermined amount

_____ 7. Place stethoscope over brachial artery

_____ 8. Record readings

_____ 9. Deflate cuff and remove from arm

_____ 10. Deflate cuff and wait 30 sec

© 2012 Cengage Learning. All Rights Reserved. May not be scanned, copied or duplicated, or posted to a publicly accessible website, in whole or in part.

Labeling
Assign the labels in the list to the appropriate places on the figure.

Figure 20-1

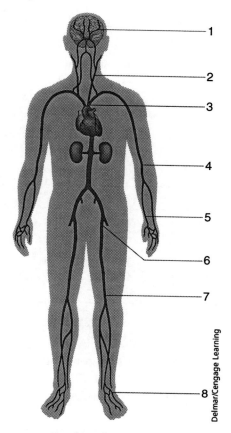

Delmar/Cengage Learning

_____ Popliteal artery

_____ Temporal artery

_____ Dorsalis pedis artery

_____ Femoral artery

_____ Brachial artery

_____ Apex (apical pulse)

_____ Carotid artery

_____ Radial artery

© 2012 Cengage Learning. All Rights Reserved. May not be scanned, copied or duplicated, or posted to a publicly accessible website, in whole or in part.

Critical Thinking Scenarios

Read each scenario. Think about the information presented in the text, and then answer each question.

1. During a physical examination of a patient the physician notes a decreased ROM of the patient's upper extremities.

    A. What is the system that is most likely being referred to in this assessment finding?

    _____

    _____

    _____

    B. What does ROM stand for?

    _____

    _____

    _____

    C. How is it assessed?

    _____

    _____

    _____

2. Mr. Andrews is complaining about shortness of breath. He says he feels like he just cannot get enough oxygen. He is a dark-skinned patient and so it is difficult to determine if he is cyanotic or not.

    A. What does cyanotic mean?

    _____

    _____

    _____

    B. How do you assess for cyanosis in a Caucasian?

    _____

    _____

    _____

    C. How do you assess for cyanosis in a dark-skinned patient?

    _____

    _____

    _____

© 2012 Cengage Learning. All Rights Reserved. May not be scanned, copied or duplicated, or posted to a publicly accessible website, in whole or in part.

D. What system is compromised in this scenario?

_____

_____

_____

Procedure Assessments

Complete the procedure assessments for this chapter at the end of the workbook.

© 2012 Cengage Learning. All Rights Reserved. May not be scanned, copied or duplicated, or posted to a publicly accessible website, in whole or in part.

CHAPTER 21

Emergency Procedures

LEARNING OBJECTIVES

Studying and applying the material in this chapter will help you to:

- Explain when first aid should be administered.
- Discuss how the Good Samaritan Act protects the rescuer.
- State the golden rule of first aid.
- Understand the seven steps to follow when an emergency occurs that will protect both the victim and rescuer.
- Identify when CPR should be performed.
- Identify illnesses and injuries that may require first aid, including their signs and symptoms and treatment.
- Demonstrate the proper application of slings and spiral, figure-eight, and finger wraps.

© 2012 Cengage Learning. All Rights Reserved. May not be scanned, copied or duplicated, or posted to a publicly accessible website, in whole or in part.

VOCABULARY REVIEW

Matching

Match the following terms with their correct definitions.

_____ 1. anaphylactic shock

_____ 2. cardiopulmonary resuscitation (CPR)

_____ 3. closed fracture

_____ 4. external bleeding

_____ 5. first aid

_____ 6. frostbite

_____ 7. golden rule

_____ 8. Good Samaritan Act

_____ 9. hemorrhage

_____ 10. hyperthermia

_____ 11. hypothermia

A. when blood drains to the outside of the body through a break in the skin

B. a primary principle when assisting others, meaning to "do no further harm"

C. condition in which the body temperature is above the normal range

D. manually providing respiratory and cardiac support for a patient who is not breathing and whose heart has stopped beating

E. a life-threatening severe allergic reaction resulting in swelling of the respiratory system that restricts breathing

F. severe, heavy bleeding

G. condition in which the body temperature is below the normal range

H. a law to protect individuals from liability when they stop to assist someone who has been hurt or is ill

I. when a bone is broken but does not protrude through the skin

J. emergency care provided to an accident victim or to someone who has become suddenly ill

K. condition in which the skin begins to freeze

Word Fill

Complete the following sentences by filling in the missing words.

internal bleeding	joint dislocation	Medic Alert	open fracture
rescue breathing	rescuer	sprains	strains
sucking wound	victim	wound	

1. A/An _____ is a person giving care during an emergency.

2. _____ is when blood loss occurs inside the body.

3. _____ are torn ligament fibers that result in a loosening of the joint.

4. _____ is when a joint becomes disconnected from its socket.

© 2012 Cengage Learning. All Rights Reserved. May not be scanned, copied or duplicated, or posted to a publicly accessible website, in whole or in part.

5. A/An _____ is a puncture into the respiratory system resulting in loss of air as the patient breathes.

6. A/An _____ is when a broken bone protrudes through the skin.

7. _____ are the result of sudden tearing of muscle fibers during exertion; also referred to as a pulled muscle.

8. A/An _____ is a person requiring care during an emergency.

9. _____ is an organization that provides bracelets or pendants for patients to wear that contain information or warnings about specific medical problems.

10. A/An _____ is damage to the soft tissue of the body as a result of violence or trauma.

11. _____ is a technique in which the rescuer breathes for the victim.

CHAPTER REVIEW

True/False

Indicate whether the following statements are true (T) or false (F).

_____ 1. First aid refers to providing emergency care to an accident victim or to someone who has suddenly become ill.

_____ 2. The American Red Cross (ARC) recommends that all health care professionals take a first aid and safety course, but it is not necessary for the general public.

_____ 3. The Good Samaritan Act requires someone to assist if they come across a victim in need of assistance.

_____ 4. You can attempt procedures you do not have the skills to perform if you feel the victim may benefit from trying.

_____ 5. Before approaching the victim, assess the situation to determine if it is safe to approach.

_____ 6. If there are hazards that would put the Good Samaritan at risk, the appropriate course of action is to not approach, but to call for help immediately.

_____ 7. Even in an emergency situation, a person has the right to refuse care.

_____ 8. Do not assume what might have occurred. If the victim is conscious, ask for information.

_____ 9. Standard precautions do not apply to emergency situations.

_____ 10. CPR, if needed, is always the first priority in any situation where first aid emergency care is given.

© 2012 Cengage Learning. All Rights Reserved. May not be scanned, copied or duplicated, or posted to a publicly accessible website, in whole or in part.

Multiple Choice

Circle the best answer for each of the following questions. There is only one correct answer to each question.

1. When is CPR administered?

   A. When someone is breathing but has no pulse
   B. When someone is not breathing but has a pulse
   C. When someone is not breathing and does not have a pulse

2. When is it appropriate to move an accident victim?

   A. If he or she gives you permission
   B. If the victim's life is in immediate danger if not moved
   C. If you can give better first aid in another location

3. Obtaining CPR training results in what type of recognition?

   A. A certificate
   B. A license
   C. An award

4. Which of the following is true about allergic reactions?

   A. They are mild and can easily be treated with an antihistamine
   B. They are life threatening and EMS should be called at the first sign of a reaction
   C. They can range from mild to life threatening

5. If a victim was stung and the stinger is visible, what is the best action to follow?

   A. Remove it by squeezing it from both sides
   B. Leave it in place
   C. Remove it by using a fingernail or credit card to scrape across it

6. What should the rescuer do if internal bleeding is suspected?

   A. Apply ice
   B. Call EMS
   C. Monitor to see if it is serious

7. What should the rescuer do if there is external bleeding?

   A. Apply pressure
   B. Check wound frequently to see if it has subsided
   C. Apply a tourniquet

8. What should the rescuer do when treating large wounds?

   A. Remove embedded objects and clean as much as possible
   B. Apply a tourniquet
   C. Remove any obvious loose debris from the wound

9. What is the characteristic of a sucking wound?

   A. Bubbling from the wound
   B. Spurting of blood from the wound
   C. Extreme pain

© 2012 Cengage Learning. All Rights Reserved. May not be scanned, copied or duplicated, or posted to a publicly accessible website, in whole or in part.

10. What should the rescuer do with an amputated part?

    A. It is not important as reattachment is not likely
    B. Pack it in ice
    C. Keep it with the victim

11. What is the purpose of a sling?

    A. Apply pressure to a wound
    B. Support injured leg, foot, or knee
    C. Support injured shoulder, collarbone, or arm

12. Where should the knot of a sling be tied?

    A. Over a bone
    B. Over soft tissue
    C. It doesn't matter

13. What is the purpose of a spiral wrap?

    A. Enhance circulation and decrease swelling
    B. Used instead of a tourniquet
    C. To restrict excessive bleeding

14. Where should you start a figure-eight wrap when applying it for an ankle injury?

    A. At the knee
    B. At the instep
    C. Midthigh

15. If the finger is broken, what should you do before applying the bandage to the finger?

    A. Apply a sling
    B. Apply a figure-eight wrap
    C. Apply a splint

Short Answer

Read each question. Think about the information presented in the text, and then answer each question.

1. What is the difference between a first, second, and third degree burn?

    _____

    _____

    _____

2. Define drug abuse.

    _____

    _____

    _____

© 2012 Cengage Learning. All Rights Reserved. May not be scanned, copied or duplicated, or posted to a publicly accessible website, in whole or in part.

3. What should the rescuer do for a drug overdose?

_____

_____

_____

4. What are the most common routes of poisonings?

_____

_____

_____

5. What are the most common sites for frostbite?

_____

_____

_____

6. How should the rescuer treat a victim with heat stroke?

_____

_____

_____

7. What is the main goal in treating hyperventilation?

_____

_____

_____

8. What is another name for chest pain? What causes it?

_____

_____

_____

9. If the victim is diabetic and it is unclear whether she is hyperglycemic or hypoglycemic, what treatment should be administered? Why?

_____

_____

_____

10. What are the three common types of seizures?

_____

_____

_____

© 2012 Cengage Learning. All Rights Reserved. May not be scanned, copied or duplicated, or posted to a publicly accessible website, in whole or in part.

Completion

Use the words in the list to complete the following statements:

Medic Alert   golden rule   eye injury   tourniquet
depth   muscle strain   rescuer; victim   Heimlich maneuver
venous; arterial   calm

1. The _____ in providing first aid is to "do no further harm."

2. The person giving care is called a _____ and the person requiring care is called the _____.

3. A form of identification called _____ may specify if the victim is diabetic, epileptic, or has specific heart problems or allergies.

4. A _____, reassuring manner in treating a victim will decrease the stress of the situation for the victim,

5. If a victim has an obstructed airway, perform the _____.

6. Do not ever apply a _____ to an extremity.

7. Blood that flows evenly from an injury is _____ bleeding. Blood that is a brighter red and comes out in spurts with each heartbeat is _____ bleeding.

8. A pulled muscle is also called a _____.

9. Any _____ should always be taken very seriously because it can involve the loss of vision.

10. The severity of the burn is determined by the size, _____, and location of the burn.

Critical Thinking Scenarios

Read each scenario. Think about the information presented in the text, and then answer each question.

1. Mr. Worthington has been in a car accident and is exhibiting signs of shock.

   A. What are the signs of shock?

   _____
   _____
   _____

   B. What causes shock?

   _____
   _____
   _____

© 2012 Cengage Learning. All Rights Reserved. May not be scanned, copied or duplicated, or posted to a publicly accessible website, in whole or in part.

C. What can the rescuer do to assist the victim?

_____

_____

_____

2. Mrs. Johnston falls to the floor at the mall due to sudden weakness on the left side of the body. The rescuer does an assessment and determines it is most likely a stroke.

A. What causes a stroke?

_____

_____

_____

B. What is a TIA?

_____

_____

_____

C. What should the rescuer do to assist the victim?

_____

_____

_____

Procedure Assessments

Complete the procedure assessments for this chapter at the end of the workbook.

© 2012 Cengage Learning. All Rights Reserved. May not be scanned, copied or duplicated, or posted to a publicly accessible website, in whole or in part.

UNIT 8
Business of Caring

© 2012 Cengage Learning. All Rights Reserved. May not be scanned, copied or duplicated, or posted to a publicly accessible website, in whole or in part.

CHAPTER 22

Controlling Health Care Costs

LEARNING OBJECTIVES

Studying and applying the material in this chapter will help you to:

- Describe how methods for paying medical costs have changed over the years.
- Contrast fee-for-service and managed care reimbursement methods.
- Explain the purpose of managed care systems and describe the methods used to control costs.
- Define Medicare, Medicaid, and DRGs.
- Identify the four major areas of expenditures incurred by a health care delivery system.
- Define accounts receivable, accounts payable, and the cost of money.
- Explain ways that the health care worker can help control facility costs.

VOCABULARY REVIEW

Definitions

Write the definition of each of the following words or terms.

1. accounts payable

_____

_____

_____

2. accounts receivable

_____

_____

_____

© 2012 Cengage Learning. All Rights Reserved. May not be scanned, copied or duplicated, or posted to a publicly accessible website, in whole or in part.

3. capitation

_____

_____

_____

4. coinsurance

_____

_____

_____

5. copay

_____

_____

_____

6. cost of money

_____

_____

_____

7. deductible

_____

_____

_____

8. diagnostic-related group (DRG)

_____

_____

_____

9. expenditures

_____

_____

_____

10. fee-for-service

_____

_____

_____

11. financing

_____

_____

_____

© 2012 Cengage Learning. All Rights Reserved. May not be scanned, copied or duplicated, or posted to a publicly accessible website, in whole or in part.

Matching 1

Match the following terms with their correct definitions.

_____ 1. gatekeeper

_____ 2. managed care

_____ 3. Medicaid

_____ 4. Medicare

_____ 5. negotiated fees

_____ 6. preauthorization

_____ 7. premium

_____ 8. prepaid plans

_____ 9. primary care provider (PCP)

_____ 10. profit

_____ 11. reimburse

A. promotion of cost-effective health care through the management and control of its delivery.

B. federally funded insurance program for individuals aged 65 and older and others, such as the disabled, who qualify for Social Security.

C. health care providers, often physicians, who serve as the patient's first contact when entering the health care system; also known as gate-keepers

D. approval from an insurance company prior to certain health care services, for the purposes of determining medical necessity and cost effec-tiveness

E. to pay back

F. a health care provider, often a physician, who serves as the patient's first contact when entering the health care system; also known as primary care provider

G. federally funded but state-administered insur-ance plan for individuals who qualify due to low income

H. an agreed-upon amount paid to an insurance company for the benefit of having the company pay for a specified amount of future health care costs

I. amount negotiated between insurance compa-nies and health care groups for the cost of services; depending on the plan, the patient either pays the difference in actual cost of service or the health care group accepts the predeter-mined amount as payment in full

J. a contracted type of insurance plan in which health care providers are paid a specific amount to provide certain health benefits

K. amount of money remaining after all costs of operating a business have been paid

© 2012 Cengage Learning. All Rights Reserved. May not be scanned, copied or duplicated, or posted to a publicly accessible website, in whole or in part.

CHAPTER REVIEW

Identification 1

Place an "X" in front of programs or regulations that are operated or initiated by the government.

_____ 1. Medicare

_____ 2. Medicaid

_____ 3. health maintenance organization (HMO)

_____ 4. exclusive provider organization (EPO)

_____ 5. preferred provider organization (PPO)

_____ 6. point-of-service plan (POS)

_____ 7. Medicare Prescription Drug, Improvement and Modernization Act (MMA) of 2003

_____ 8. diagnostic-related groups (DRGs)

Identification 2

Place an "X" in front of services that may apply to Part B of Medicare.

_____ 1. hospital stay

_____ 2. skilled facility following a hospital stay

_____ 3. outpatient medical supplies

_____ 4. inpatient diagnostic tests

_____ 5. hospice care

_____ 6. outpatient physical and occupational therapy

_____ 7. home health

_____ 8. outpatient prescription drugs

_____ 9. HMO or PPO organizations

_____ 10. physician's fee for office visit

True/False

Indicate whether the following statements are true (T) or false (F).

_____ 1. A major concern in the United States today is how to effectively control dramatically rising health care costs.

_____ 2. Health care costs are evenly distributed among all patients.

_____ 3. Chronic conditions are seen only in the aged.

© 2012 Cengage Learning. All Rights Reserved. May not be scanned, copied or duplicated, or posted to a publicly accessible website, in whole or in part.

_____ 4. More money is spent per person on health care in the United States than in any other country.

_____ 5. The youth of this nation are showing an alarming increase in obesity, poor diet, and lack of physical fitness.

_____ 6. Prepaid plans are based on the idea that providers can be motivated to be more efficient.

_____ 7. Insurance coverage is based on the concept of those who need the service will pay more.

_____ 8. Medicare is free and covers all medical expenses.

_____ 9. Medicare has a monthly premium along with deductibles and coinsurance amounts.

_____ 10. Medicaid is a cost assistance program to help pay the medical costs for those who qualify due to low income.

Matching 2

Match the following terms with their correct definitions.

_____ 1. HMO (health maintenance organization)

_____ 2. EPO (exclusive provider organization)

_____ 3. PPO (preferred provider organization)

_____ 4. POS (point-of-service plan)

_____ 5. another name for gatekeepers

_____ 6. Medicare

_____ 7. Medigap

_____ 8. generic

_____ 9. accounts receivable

_____ 10. personnel

A. greater flexibility than an HMO to create a benefits package specific to company's needs

B. a group of hospitals and physicians who contract on a fee-for-service basis

C. administered by the Centers for Medicare & Medicaid Services (CMS).

D. members can choose to receive a service from participating or nonparticipating providers

E. prepaid medical group practice plan that provides a predetermined medical care benefit package

F. primary care providers (PCP)

G. often the largest cost incurred by a facility

H. supplemental insurance policy for costs not included under Medicare

I. these drugs are less expensive than brand names

J. a sound business practice is to keep this as low as possible

© 2012 Cengage Learning. All Rights Reserved. May not be scanned, copied or duplicated, or posted to a publicly accessible website, in whole or in part.

Short Answer

Read each question. Think about the information presented in the text, and then answer each question.

1. Why did the fee-for-service plan go out of favor?

   _____

   _____

   _____

2. Discuss the three methods that have been devised to reduce overuse of services by patients.

   _____

   _____

   _____

3. What is preauthorization? Why is it important for the health care professional to know when it is required?

   _____

   _____

   _____

4. What is the purpose of Medicare? What are Parts A, B, C, and D?

   _____

   _____

   _____

5. Explain how DRGs (diagnostic-related groups) came about and how they work.

   _____

   _____

   _____

6. Health care facilities' expenditures occur in what four major areas?

   _____

   _____

   _____

7. List four ways that the health care professional can contribute to the efficient and cost-effective functioning of the facility.

   _____

   _____

   _____

© 2012 Cengage Learning. All Rights Reserved. May not be scanned, copied or duplicated, or posted to a publicly accessible website, in whole or in part.

8. What is the most likely cause when employees have difficulty performing efficiently?

   _____

   _____

   _____

9. How can the use of a problem-solving process help the employee improve efficiency?

   _____

   _____

   _____

10. What four questions can employees ask themselves when they are wanting to help reduce unnecessary costs?

    _____

    _____

    _____

Completion

Use the words in the list to complete the following statements.

Physician; insurance company	prepaid	expenditures	premium
managed care	primary care providers (PCP)	copay	financing resources
		capitation	profit

1. Paying an insurance company an agreed-upon amount for coverage is called a _____.

2. A fee-for-service plan is when the _____ determines what actions to take and the _____ pays for the services.

3. _____ contain specific built-in cost controls.

4. A _____ is the amount of money remaining after all costs of operating a business have been paid.

5. In _____ plans, health care providers are paid before rather than after services are performed.

6. When the provider is paid the same regardless of the type or number of services provided, the method of payment is called _____.

7. A _____ is paying a set amount for each visit or service.

8. One method that has been devised to reduce the overuse of services by patients is the use of _____.

9. _____ refer to any money that is spent in the process of doing business.

10. _____ for a health care facility come primarily from a variety of health insurance companies

© 2012 Cengage Learning. All Rights Reserved. May not be scanned, copied or duplicated, or posted to a publicly accessible website, in whole or in part.

Critical Thinking Scenarios

Read each scenario. Think about the information presented in the text, and then answer each question.

1. Maria Torres just started working in a new health care facility. She notes that her co-workers take excessive breaks and is concerned about the impact it has on patient care.

   A. What impact does her coworkers' behavior have on Maria?

   _____

   _____

   _____

   B. What impact does her coworkers' behavior have on patient care?

   _____

   _____

   _____

   C. What impact does it have on the facility's ability to function?

   _____

   _____

   _____

2. Mr. Gerald Beuller is trying to decide what insurance policy he should choose. He finds it very confusing and angrily states "between the deductibles, copays, and coinsurance it seems I am paying for everything."

   A. What is a deductible?

   _____

   _____

   _____

   B. What is coinsurance?

   _____

   _____

   _____

   C. What is a copay?

   _____

   _____

   _____

© 2012 Cengage Learning. All Rights Reserved. May not be scanned, copied or duplicated, or posted to a publicly accessible website, in whole or in part.

CHAPTER 23

Performance Improvement and Customer Service

LEARNING OBJECTIVES

Studying and applying the material in this chapter will help you to:

■ Understand the components used in determining quality of care.

■ Explain what is meant by quality improvement.

■ Identify the internal and external customers in a health care setting.

■ Describe the steps in working with unhappy customers.

■ Describe the characteristics of constructive criticism.

■ Discuss how a health care worker can view destructive criticism in a constructive manner.

VOCABULARY REVIEW

Definitions

Write the definition of each of the following words or terms.

1. constructive criticism

   _____

   _____

   _____

2. external customers

   _____

   _____

   _____

© 2012 Cengage Learning. All Rights Reserved. May not be scanned, copied or duplicated, or posted to a publicly accessible website, in whole or in part.

3. internal customers

_____

_____

_____

4. quality improvement

_____

_____

_____

CHAPTER REVIEW

True/False

Indicate whether the following statements are true (T) or false (F).

_____ 1. Health care workers must ask themselves what they can do to best meet the needs of the organization, their coworkers, and patients.

_____ 2. When the term "customer" is used, it refers to both internal and external customers.

_____ 3. Outside suppliers of medical and pharmaceutical supplies are considered external customers.

_____ 4. Education would be considered a prevention service.

_____ 5. When a patient evaluates the service received, it is not just the outcome that is important, but the entire experience.

_____ 6. Most facilities have stopped using customer satisfaction surveys as it is more important to look at patient outcomes.

_____ 7. Each health care professional is responsible for patient satisfaction.

_____ 8. Satisfaction is an objective perception.

_____ 9. When people take pride in their work, they will work harder and more cooperatively than they will if they feel that others are being overly critical.

_____ 10. Criticism should not be given to coworkers as it breaks down the working relationship.

© 2012 Cengage Learning. All Rights Reserved. May not be scanned, copied or duplicated, or posted to a publicly accessible website, in whole or in part.

True/False Rewrite

Please rewrite the bold part of the sentence to make the statement true.

1. With the advent of modern health care practices, **it is relatively easy to find the balance between maintaining high-quality patient care and controlling costs.**

_____

_____

_____

2. Spending more on health care **results in better quality of care.**

_____

_____

_____

3. The CMS (Centers for Medicare & Medicaid Services) impacts **only those patients who are on Medicare or Medicaid.**

_____

_____

_____

4. Utilization review (UR) is **a data-collection-only organization.**

_____

_____

_____

5. Patients are an example of an **internal** customer.

_____

_____

_____

6. External customers are those **who work in the health care industry.**

_____

_____

_____

7. **Inpatient services** include nursing homes and assisted living.

_____

_____

_____

8. Illnesses and injuries requiring continuous acute care are considered **emergency and urgent care services**.

_____

_____

_____

© 2012 Cengage Learning. All Rights Reserved. May not be scanned, copied or duplicated, or posted to a publicly accessible website, in whole or in part.

9. Lawsuits are **primarily based on medical errors**.

_____

_____

_____

10. When working with an unhappy customer, **it is best to postpone the conversation until the customer cools off**.

_____

_____

_____

Multiple Choice

Circle the best answer for each of the following questions. There is only one correct answer to each question.

1. Which country ranks highest in health care expenditures?

   A. United States
   B. France
   C. Canada

2. Which of the following is true about American's satisfaction with their health care?

   A. Most are satisfied
   B. Many are dissatisfied
   C. Few are dissatisfied

3. Who performs the UR (utilization review) services?

   A. Peer review group or public agency
   B. Board of directors
   C. Governmental agencies

4. What are the UR (utilization review) criteria based upon?

   A. On the money available for patient care
   B. Mutual agreement with providers
   C. Protocols, benchmarks, or other data

5. Which of the following is true about a QIO (Quality Improvement Organization)?

   A. CMS (Centers for Medicare & Medicaid Services) contracts with one organization in each county.
   B. They are private, mostly not-for-profit organizations.
   C. They are staffed primarily by lay public.

6. What is the first step when working with unhappy customers?

   A. Call the supervisor
   B. Identify the problem
   C. Explain to the customer why it happened

© 2012 Cengage Learning. All Rights Reserved. May not be scanned, copied or duplicated, or posted to a publicly accessible website, in whole or in part.

7. What is the second step when working with unhappy customers?

   A. Seek resolution
   B. Clarify what the problem is
   C. Assure the customer that the person responsible will be reprimanded

8. What is the last step when working with unhappy customers?

   A. Tell the customer it won't happen again
   B. Apologize profusely
   C. Verify satisfaction

9. What is constructive criticism based on?

   A. Clarifying the lines of authority
   B. Making sure others are quickly corrected
   C. Optimism

10. Which of the following is a technique that can be used when giving constructive criticism?

    A. Sandwich
    B. Telling it like it is
    C. Honesty above all else

Short Answer

Read each question. Think about the information presented in the text, and then answer each question.

1. What are the two primary questions that need to be asked when discussing how to improve the quality of care and raise patient satisfaction?

   _____

   _____

   _____

2. What are three factors to consider when trying to measure quality of care?

   _____

   _____

   _____

3. What are the shortcomings of the factors listed in question #2?

   _____

   _____

   _____

© 2012 Cengage Learning. All Rights Reserved. May not be scanned, copied or duplicated, or posted to a publicly accessible website, in whole or in part.

4. In health care the goal is 100% correct care with no errors. Is this realistic? What are the possible consequences if not obtained?

_____

_____

_____

5. What is the process involved in quality improvement?

_____

_____

_____

6. Who is CMS (Centers for Medicare and Medicaid Services)?

_____

_____

_____

7. Why was CMS (Centers for Medicare and Medicaid Services) designed?

_____

_____

_____

8. What does the CMS (Centers for Medicare and Medicaid Services) require of all health care facilities?

_____

_____

_____

9. The CMS requires all health care facilities to establish a QAPI program that demonstrates a commitment to the goal of ensuring high-quality and cost-effective care. What does the abbreviation QAPI stand for?

_____

_____

_____

10. What are the three primary areas to examine when evaluating a health care facility for quality improvement?

_____

_____

_____

© 2012 Cengage Learning. All Rights Reserved. May not be scanned, copied or duplicated, or posted to a publicly accessible website, in whole or in part.

Critical Thinking Scenarios

Read each scenario. Think about the information presented in the text, and then answer each question.

1. Ms. Jerkins is furious when a coworker arrives late from lunch. The patients are upset as they are still waiting for services.

   A. What impact is the employee who is late having on the facility?

   _____
   _____
   _____

   B. Should Ms. Jenkins speak the coworker? If so, when?

   _____
   _____
   _____

   C. What is the difference between constructive and destructive criticism?

   _____
   _____
   _____

2. Mrs. Tomlison calls and states her husband is having chest pain, nausea, and some difficulty breathing. She requests an appointment at the clinic to see his primary care provider.

   A. Should she be given an appointment as requested?

   _____
   _____
   _____

   B. What level of care does the clinic provide?

   _____
   _____
   _____

   C. What level of care does the patient need in this case?

   _____
   _____
   _____

© 2012 Cengage Learning. All Rights Reserved. May not be scanned, copied or duplicated, or posted to a publicly accessible website, in whole or in part.

UNIT 9
Securing and Maintaining Employment

© 2012 Cengage Learning. All Rights Reserved. May not be scanned, copied or duplicated, or posted to a publicly accessible website, in whole or in part.

CHAPTER 24

Job Leads and the Resume

LEARNING OBJECTIVES

Studying and applying the material in this chapter will help you to:

- Develop an inventory of your employment skills and personal traits that are of value to an employer.
- Identify your workplace preferences.
- Describe ways to get organized for the job search.
- List the most common sources of job leads and explain how to use each one effectively.
- Create a resume that highlights your qualifications and encourages employers to interview you.
- Write effective cover letters to accompany your resume.

VOCABULARY REVIEW

Matching

Match the following terms with their correct definitions.

_____ 1. chronological resume	A.	emphasizes professional qualifications rather than work history
_____ 2. cover letter	B.	emphasizes work experience
_____ 3. functional resume	C.	personal characteristics
_____ 4. objective	D.	job goal
_____ 5. resume	E.	introductory document
_____ 6. traits	F.	summary of professional qualifications

© 2012 Cengage Learning. All Rights Reserved. May not be scanned, copied or duplicated, or posted to a publicly accessible website, in whole or in part.

Word Fill

Complete the following sentences by filling in the missing words.

networking   cold calling   career service centers   joblines

1. Schools provide _____ to help graduates obtain employment.

2. _____ takes some confidence, but it can be an effective way to discover unadvertised job openings.

3. Recorded information on _____ enables job seekers to learn about openings at a specific facility.

4. Connecting with other people through _____ has helped many job seekers start successful careers.

CHAPTER REVIEW

Identification

Place an "X" in front of the sections of a resume that are optional.

_____ 1. special skills

_____ 2. awards and honors

_____ 3. heading

_____ 4. membership in professional organizations

_____ 5. objective

_____ 6. work history

_____ 7. hobbies and special interests

_____ 8. volunteer work

_____ 9. qualifications

_____ 10. education

True/False Rewrite

Please rewrite the bold part of the sentence to make the statement true.

1. Career professionals recommend that job seekers spend about **10 hours** a week on their job search.

    _____

    _____

    _____

© 2012 Cengage Learning. All Rights Reserved. May not be scanned, copied or duplicated, or posted to a publicly accessible website, in whole or in part.

2. The job search can be difficult because job seekers are **powerless** and must depend on employers to offer them employment.

_____

_____

_____

3. When seeking a first-time job, your personal preferences should be a **low priority**.

_____

_____

_____

4. A good way to determine what kind of salary you need to earn is to estimate what you spend in **one month**.

_____

_____

_____

5. Although schools try to help their graduates, only about **15 percent** actually find employment because of their efforts.

_____

_____

_____

6. If your school schedules an interview for you, but the position doesn't sound interesting, it is acceptable to **not attend** the interview.

_____

_____

_____

7. The reason for attending a job fair is to **interview with as many employers as possible**.

_____

_____

_____

8. Today's most effective way to obtain a job is to **post one's resume on the Internet**.

_____

_____

_____

9. In most cases, a **chronological** resume is the best choice for recent graduates who have no previous health care experience.

_____

_____

_____

© 2012 Cengage Learning. All Rights Reserved. May not be scanned, copied or duplicated, or posted to a publicly accessible website, in whole or in part.

10. The purpose of a resume is to convince an employer to **hire you**.

_____

_____

_____

Multiple Choice

Circle the best answer for each of the following questions. There is only one correct answer to each question.

1. If an ad for a job says, "no calls," it is recommended that you _____.

   A. not call because calling shows your inability to follow instructions
   B. call anyway because this shows you are motivated
   C. not consider this job because the employer does not seem serious

2. The first step when starting your job search is to _____.

   A. consider all the qualifications you have to offer an employer
   B. prepare an outline for your resume
   C. decide what kind of job you want

3. Most employers are interested in hiring graduates who have _____.

   A. years of experience in health care
   B. highly developed technical skills
   C. both technical skills and good communication skills

4. The purpose of The Riley Guide at www.rileyguide.com is to _____.

   A. give applicants an opportunity to post their resumes
   B. provide links to health care employers
   C. provide links to websites on all types of career and employment topics

5. Jason plans to use the Internet to make his resume available for employers. Which of the following websites would most likely result in an interview for Jason?

   A. A national general resume-posting site
   B. A health care resume-posting site
   C. A local health care facility's website

6. Prior to enrolling in a nursing program, Liz worked as a preschool teacher. Her best choice would be a _____ resume.

   A. chronological
   B. functional
   C. professional

7. A cover letter should be included with your resume _____.

   A. any time you submit it to an employer
   B. in response to an unadvertised position
   C. when a cover letter is requested

© 2012 Cengage Learning. All Rights Reserved. May not be scanned, copied or duplicated, or posted to a publicly accessible website, in whole or in part.

8. Which of the following information should be included in your resume?

   A. Your marital status
   B. Your telephone number
   C. The statement "references available"

9. Which of the following objectives would target the largest number of job openings?

   A. Position as a surgical technologist
   B. Position as a surgical technologist in an ambulatory surgery center
   C. Position as a surgical technologist in an orthopedic surgery center

10. Which of the following would best fit in the Qualifications section of a resume for a graduate seeking a position as a physical therapist assistant?

    A. Earned a 3.7/4.0 grade point average in my physical therapist courses
    B. Taught exercise classes at a senior center for 3 years
    C. Clinical internship at Get Strong Physical Therapy Clinic, Eugene, Oregon

Short Answer

Read each question. Think about the information presented in the text, and then answer each question.

1. What are nine factors you should consider when thinking about the type of facility in which you want to work?

   _____
   _____
   _____

2. List six categories of expenses you should consider when calculating your basic living expenses.

   _____
   _____
   _____

3. Why is it important to have an appropriate message on your answering machine or service?

   _____
   _____
   _____

4. What is Career One Stop?

   _____
   _____
   _____

© 2012 Cengage Learning. All Rights Reserved. May not be scanned, copied or duplicated, or posted to a publicly accessible website, in whole or in part.

5. What are three types of networking contacts job seekers can develop?

   _____

   _____

   _____

6. List five ways you can use the Internet in your job search.

   _____

   _____

   _____

7. If you decide to post your resume on the Internet, what should *never* be included on the resume?

   _____

   _____

   _____

8. Why is it recommended that learners write their own resumes rather than having them prepared by a resume service?

   _____

   _____

   _____

9. What four items should be included in the heading of your resume?

   _____

   _____

   _____

10. How should your resume be altered if it will be electronically scanned by an employer?

   _____

   _____

   _____

© 2012 Cengage Learning. All Rights Reserved. May not be scanned, copied or duplicated, or posted to a publicly accessible website, in whole or in part.

Critical Thinking Scenarios

Read each scenario. Think about the information presented in the text, and then answer each question.

1. Angie has just completed her medical coder course and is eager to get to work. However, she is feeling a little overwhelmed by the job search and is not sure about the best way to find good job leads.

   A. Who should Angie contact first to get started finding leads?

   _____

   _____

   _____

   B. What kinds of websites would likely be most helpful?

   _____

   _____

   _____

   C. What is the web address for the U.S. Department of Labor's website for job hunters?

   _____

   _____

   _____

2. Andy entered community college directly from high school and has little work experience in any field other than working part-time in a supermarket. He has almost completed his EMT training and is starting to put together his resume.

   A. Which type of resume would be the best for Andy? Explain why.

   _____

   _____

   _____

   B. Which section, after the heading and objective, should he place at the beginning of his resume? Explain why.

   _____

   _____

   _____

© 2012 Cengage Learning. All Rights Reserved. May not be scanned, copied or duplicated, or posted to a publicly accessible website, in whole or in part.

CHAPTER 25

Interview, Portfolio, and Application

LEARNING OBJECTIVES

Studying and applying the material in this chapter will help you to:

- Explain the purpose of the job interview.
- Describe how to obtain background information about employers and health care organizations.
- Create examples to illustrate your employment qualifications.
- Prepare appropriate questions to ask at interviews.
- Anticipate and prepare for questions that may be asked at interviews.
- Describe ways to handle illegal questions asked by employers.
- Demonstrate successful interview behavior and appearance.
- Identify references who will support your job search efforts.
- Create a reference list to give to potential employers.
- Build a professional portfolio to provide evidence of your job skills and qualifications.
- Explain what actions to take after an interview to increase your chances of being hired.
- Explain how to accept and reject job offers.

© 2012 Cengage Learning. All Rights Reserved. May not be scanned, copied or duplicated, or posted to a publicly accessible website, in whole or in part.

VOCABULARY REVIEW

Word Fill

Complete the following sentences by filling in the missing words.

job interview	references	illegal questions	situational question
letter of recommendation	portfolio	reference list	behavioral questions

1. Employers now use _____ to learn how applicants have handled workplace problems in the past.

2. Employers cannot use information obtained from _____ to make hiring decisions.

3. The purpose of the _____ is for employers and applicants to learn about each other.

4. It is a good idea to ask for a/an _____ whenever you leave a job on good terms.

5. A collection of documents you might use at an interview to support your qualifications is called a/an _____.

6. Be sure to ask your _____ for permission before giving their names to prospective employers.

7. Your _____ contains the names and contact information of people who will vouch for your qualifications.

8. An example of a/an _____ is, "Tell me about how you would handle working with a rude patient."

CHAPTER REVIEW

True/False

Indicate whether the following statements are true (T) or false (F).

_____ 1. Job applicants can best present themselves at interviews by being modest and courteous.

_____ 2. The interview is a good time to ask for a job description of the position you are applying for.

_____ 3. Applicants should prepare questions in advance to ask at an interview.

_____ 4. Asking about benefits and vacation days is appropriate at the first interview for a job.

_____ 5. If an employer asks you about your weaknesses, it is best to state that you really can't think of any.

_____ 6. Your appearance makes an important statement about you as a professional.

© 2012 Cengage Learning. All Rights Reserved. May not be scanned, copied or duplicated, or posted to a publicly accessible website, in whole or in part.

_____ 7. Perfumes that most people find pleasant can be offensive to people who are ill.

_____ 8. Some employers are becoming more accepting of tattoos and piercings on health care professionals.

_____ 9. Your portfolio contains documents that should be sent along with your resume.

_____ 10. Listening at an interview is just as important as speaking well.

_____ 11. It is illegal for employers to require job applicants to be tested for drugs.

_____ 12. If you are offered a job that you decide you don't want, it is recommended that you explain why you are not accepting it.

Multiple Choice

Circle the best answer for each of the following questions. There is only one correct answer to each question.

1. Which of the following best describes the purpose of a job interview?

   A. It is a time for employers to ask questions and find out if applicants fill their requirements.
   B. It gives applicants a chance to learn about a job.
   C. It gives applicants and employers an opportunity to get to know each other.

2. Which action on the part of applicants is most likely to help them do well at job interviews?

   A. Participate in mock interviews
   B. Write a great resume
   C. Put together a good portfolio

3. Which of the following reasons most likely accounts for recent graduates' failure to get hired?

   A. They do not have work experience.
   B. They lack the necessary technical skills.
   C. They do not sell themselves well.

4. The reason for creating a personal inventory of skills and traits is to _____.

   A. build your confidence for interviewing and asking for a job
   B. give you examples to demonstrate and support your skills
   C. have a written list to give to employers

5. Which of the following questions would be most appropriate for an applicant to ask at an interview for a job in a small, single-physician office?

   A. "What are the opportunities for promotion?"
   B. "What type of orientation would I receive?"
   C. "How much would I be earning after a year of work?"

6. The best answers to behavioral questions consist of a/an _____.

   A. description of a past experience
   B. short answer that is to the point
   C. explanation of how you have improved

© 2012 Cengage Learning. All Rights Reserved. May not be scanned, copied or duplicated, or posted to a publicly accessible website, in whole or in part.

7. Which of the following is an example of an illegal question?

    A. "Where are your parents from?"
    B. "Can you work nights?"
    C. "How do you handle stressful situations?"

8. John was fired from his last job for taking too many breaks. Which is his best response if a prospective employer asks if he has ever been fired?

    A. "No, I haven't."
    B. "Yes, my last boss really didn't like me."
    C. "Yes. I used to take too many smoke breaks. I have since quit smoking and started an exercise program, so this is no longer a problem for me."

9. Jan, a single mother with three school-age children, is interviewing for a job she really wants. If the employer asks her if she has young children, it would be best for her to state, "_____."

    A. That question is illegal
    B. I don't have to answer questions about my family
    C. I have children and have arranged for very dependable child-care

10. Which of the following would be the best person to ask to write you a letter of recommendation?

    A. A family friend who has known you since childhood
    B. The supervisor at your extern site
    C. Your dentist

Matching

Match the following terms with the example that best illustrates it.

_____ 1. general question   A. is Friday casual dress day?

_____ 2. illegal question   B. have you ever been arrested?

_____ 3. behavioral question   C. can you tell me why you've had so many jobs?

_____ 4. information about employer   D. I chaired a committee that raised over $10,000 for my children's school.

_____ 5. appropriate question to ask employer   E. hospital website

_____ 6. question to avoid   F. why do you want to work here?

_____ 7. supportive example   G. tell me the steps you would take to clean up a blood spill.

_____ 8. health-care question   H. criminal background check

_____ 9. question to answer honestly   I. tell me about a conflict you've had with a coworker and how you resolved it.

_____ 10. possible hiring requirement   J. what is a typical day like for someone in this position?

© 2012 Cengage Learning. All Rights Reserved. May not be scanned, copied or duplicated, or posted to a publicly accessible website, in whole or in part.

Short Answer

Read each question. Think about the information presented in the text, and then answer each question.

1. Why do some employers find the interview process to be a stressful experience?

   _____

   _____

   _____

2. What are three reasons for learning about an employer before attending an interview?

   _____

   _____

   _____

3. List four sources you might use to learn about prospective employers.

   _____

   _____

   _____

4. What is the best way to inform an employer about your various skills?

   _____

   _____

   _____

5. When answering general questions such as, "Tell me about yourself," what should you be sure to include in your answer?

   _____

   _____

   _____

6. List five items that would be appropriate to include in your portfolio.

   _____

   _____

   _____

7. What three actions should you take when you meet the person who will interview you?

   _____

   _____

   _____

8. Why is it important for a job applicant to be courteous with the receptionist when arriving for an interview?

   _____

   _____

   _____

9. Under what circumstances should you send a thank-you note following an interview?

_____

_____

_____

10. What are eight guidelines for correctly filling out an employment application?

_____

_____

_____

Critical Thinking Scenarios

Read each scenario. Think about the information presented in the text, and then answer each question.

1. Chad is interviewing for a job as a physical therapist assistant. The employer asks what part of town he lives in.

    A. Is this an appropriate question for the employer to ask? Explain.

    _____

    _____

    _____

    B. Why might the employer ask this question?

    _____

    _____

    _____

    C. How should Chad respond?

    _____

    _____

    _____

2. Kayla interviewed for a job in health information management at the clinic where her own doctor practices. This was a job she really wanted and she felt she interviewed well. However, she just received word that she did not get the job.

    A. What are possible reasons why Kayla was not offered this job?

    _____

    _____

    _____

    B. What should Kayla do now?

    _____

    _____

    _____

    C. What should Kayla do if she attends many interviews and fails to receive a job offer?

    _____

    _____

    _____

© 2012 Cengage Learning. All Rights Reserved. May not be scanned, copied or duplicated, or posted to a publicly accessible website, in whole or in part.

CHAPTER 26

Successful Employment Strategies

LEARNING OBJECTIVES

Studying and applying the material in this chapter will help you to:

- Identify important information that new employees should learn about the facility in which they work.
- Explain the importance of understanding the facility's policies and procedures.
- Explain the purpose of the probationary period.
- Identify seven behaviors that contribute to professional success.
- List and describe the major laws that affect hiring and employment practices.
- Explain the meaning of a grievance and how it should be handled.
- Explain the meaning of sexual harassment and the actions to take if it occurs.
- Describe a typical performance evaluation.
- Identify the steps to take when leaving a job voluntarily.
- Describe ways to cope with being fired from a job.
- List activities that promote professional development of the health care professional.

© 2012 Cengage Learning. All Rights Reserved. May not be scanned, copied or duplicated, or posted to a publicly accessible website, in whole or in part.

VOCABULARY REVIEW

Matching 1

Match the following terms with their correct definitions.

_____ 1. chain of command

_____ 2. grievance

_____ 3. minimum wage

_____ 4. policy

_____ 5. procedure

_____ 6. reasonable accommodation

_____ 7. risk management

_____ 8. sexual harassment

A. correct way to perform a task

B. plans and methods to ensure safety

C. least amount of pay legally allowed

D. change that enables a disabled person to work

E. levels of authority and reporting

F. unwelcome and/or offensive actions

G. established rule or course of action

H. formal complaint

Word Fill

Complete the following sentences by filling in the missing words.

employee manual   integrity   professional   job description
role model   probationary period   development   mentor
team   performance evaluation

1. Having a _____ to give you information and encouragement can contribute to a successful career.

2. Review your _____ carefully so you know what your duties are.

3. The _____ gives the employer and employee a chance to see how things are working out for each of them.

4. _____ includes activities that help you improve your career knowledge and performance.

5. New hires are likely to be part of a/an _____ of professionals working together.

6. A/an _____ serves as a positive example of professional actions.

7. Check the _____ to learn about the organization in which you work.

8. Going through a/an _____ helps both you and your employer track your progress.

9. Honesty and morality are signs of _____, an important quality for health care professionals.

© 2012 Cengage Learning. All Rights Reserved. May not be scanned, copied or duplicated, or posted to a publicly accessible website, in whole or in part.

CHAPTER REVIEW

True/False

Indicate whether the following statements are true (T) or false (F).

_____ 1. Failure to follow safety policies can be grounds for dismissal from a job.

_____ 2. In many states, employees can be dismissed for any reason during the probationary period.

_____ 3. Achieving personal success is generally all that is expected of an employee.

_____ 4. Having many points of view, as with the members of a work team, makes completing projects an inefficient and difficult process.

_____ 5. New employees are not really expected to make contributions to workplace teams.

_____ 6. Knowing when to ask for help is an important work skill.

_____ 7. It is generally necessary to do more than the minimum job requirements to achieve career success.

_____ 8. A good strategy at work is to avoid problems whenever possible.

_____ 9. Performance evaluations do not always include a salary review.

_____ 10. Employees should be prepared to argue and defend themselves if they receive low ratings in their performance evaluation.

_____ 11. Employees have the right to view the contents of their personnel files.

_____ 12. When leaving a job, it is recommended that you state your reasons for quitting, including complaints that were not resolved.

_____ 13. It is usually advisable to find a new job before leaving the present one.

_____ 14. Failure to follow standard practices can be a cause for dismissal.

_____ 15. One week's notice is usually adequate when leaving a job.

Multiple Choice

Circle the best answer for each of the following questions. There is only one correct answer to each question.

1. Which is the most important reason for following a facility's policies and procedures?
   A. They give consistency to the facility's operations.
   B. They may be legally required.
   C. They give your supervisor a way to measure your performance.

© 2012 Cengage Learning. All Rights Reserved. May not be scanned, copied or duplicated, or posted to a publicly accessible website, in whole or in part.

2. Information about paid holidays would most likely be found in a/an _____.

   A. employee manual
   B. handbook of procedures
   C. job description

3. "Assist the physician during surgical procedures" is an example of a _____.

   A. working condition
   B. minimum requirement
   C. responsibility

4. The main purpose of the probationary period is to _____.

   A. determine if the employee should receive a raise
   B. teach the employee needed job skills
   C. give the employer a chance to evaluate the employee

5. Which of the following is the best example of an employee demonstrating integrity?

   A. Amy always greets patients with a smile and friendly greeting.
   B. John forgot to make an important note on a patient chart and he tells the physician as soon as he realizes his mistake.
   C. Sarah takes extra time to explain procedures to patients to help them feel more comfortable and less anxious.

6. Which of the following behaviors best demonstrates loyalty to the employer?

   A. Dan told his boss that he needed clearer instructions about his assigned duties.
   B. Liz keeps the problems she's having with her supervisor to herself.
   C. Lauren lets off steam about her supervisor to her husband after work.

7. Observing the chain of command means to _____.

   A. warn your supervisor's boss about problems in your department
   B. report problems to your supervisor
   C. share problems with your coworkers

8. When would it acceptable to make personal phone calls during work hours?

   A. If you have a family emergency
   B. When you don't have work to do
   C. It is never acceptable

9. If you tend to procrastinate when faced with a large task, it is recommended that you _____.

   A. start with the easiest part first
   B. get started and push to do as much as possible
   C. break the task down into manageable parts

10. If you have a personal conflict with a team member, it is best to _____.

    A. keep the matter to yourself
    B. discuss the matter with the team member in private
    C. bring the matter into the open at a team meeting

© 2012 Cengage Learning. All Rights Reserved. May not be scanned, copied or duplicated, or posted to a publicly accessible website, in whole or in part.

Matching 2

Match the following terms with the examples that best illustrate them.

—— 1. Title VII of 1964 Civil Rights Act

A. BeWell Health Clinic cannot refuse to hire applicants because they are not Christian.

—— 2. Family Medical Leave Act

B. Happy Home Health cannot hire aides who do not have the legal right to work in the United States.

—— 3. Americans with Disabilities Act

C. Good Care Hospital cannot deny employment to a qualified medical coder because she has a hearing impairment.

—— 4. Equal Pay Act of 1963

D. Dr. Cromwell must pay his medical assistant no less than what his state requires.

—— 5. minimum wage laws

E. Molly uses this after being unsuccessful in resolving what she believes to be unfair treatment from her supervisor.

—— 6. Civil Rights Act of 1964

F. Ashley wants to take a few weeks off after the birth of her child.

—— 7. Occupational Safety and Health Act

G. Ellie advises her supervisor that his unwanted comments about her "sexy" appearance are violating her legal rights.

—— 8. grievance procedure

H. Good Care Hospital provides free hepatitis B immunizations for all employees who provide direct patient care.

—— 9. Immigration Reform Act

I. The Caring Clinic must pay Carol and Tim, both medical assistants with four years of experience, the same salary.

Critical Thinking Scenarios

Read each scenario. Think about the information presented in the text, and then answer each question.

1. Roberto has been working at LiveWell Center for three years. During the past six months, he has been feeling dissatisfied with his job and wonders if he should look for a new one.

   A. In making his decision, what should Roberto do first?

   _____

   _____

   _____

© 2012 Cengage Learning. All Rights Reserved. May not be scanned, copied or duplicated, or posted to a publicly accessible website, in whole or in part.

B. What factors should he consider when comparing his current job with other possibilities?

_____

_____

_____

C. If Roberto decides to leave his job, how should he proceed?

_____

_____

_____

2. Andrea has been working at her first job as a medical sonographer for two weeks. Her position had been vacant for some time and the supervisor did not have a lot of time to give her an orientation to the facility.

A. What are sources of information that Andrea might use to learn more about the facility and what she is expected to do?

_____

_____

_____

B. Why is it important for her to pay special attention to the facility's risk management policies?

_____

_____

_____

C. As a new employee, when should Andrea expect to have her first employment evaluation?

_____

_____

_____

© 2012 Cengage Learning. All Rights Reserved. May not be scanned, copied or duplicated, or posted to a publicly accessible website, in whole or in part.

Completion

Use the words in the list to complete the following statements:

enthusiasm   policy   role model   quality control

flexibility   professional   supervisor   networking

performance   development

evaluation   sexual harassment

1. Proofreading a report written for work and correcting any errors is an example of _____.

2. Signs of _____ are being passionate about and interested in your work.

3. Identifying a/an _____ at your first job can help you learn how to be a true professional in your occupation.

4. Telling off-color jokes in the presence of someone who finds them offensive is a form of _____.

5. Employees can improve their work performance by actively participating in their _____.

6. When quitting a job, you should first advise your _____.

7. Many workplaces have a/an _____ that requires a supervisor to observe a fired employee as he or she packs up personal belongings.

8. An important part of _____ is setting goals and learning new skills.

9. _____ should be carried out throughout your career both for your own benefit and that of others.

10. Health care professionals should demonstrate _____ by responding well to changing conditions in the workplace.

© 2012 Cengage Learning. All Rights Reserved. May not be scanned, copied or duplicated, or posted to a publicly accessible website, in whole or in part.